The New Pub League Quiz Book Number 2

QuizMasters of Great Britain

David Duncan

foulsham

LONDON • NEW YORK • TORONTO • SYDNEY

foulsham

The Publishing House, Bennetts Close,
Cippenham, Berkshire SL1 5AP

ISBN 0-572-02433-9

Typeset in Great Britain by Grafica, Bournemouth
Printed in Great Britain at St Edmundsbury Press, Bury St Edmunds

Contents

The Pub League Quizzes

The Answers

The Pub League Quizzes

Rules of the Game

These exciting quizzes are taken from the Quiz Masters Pub League quizzes. They are great fun to play at home with any number of team members, or you can use the correct pub league rules and try out the quizzes at your local.

If you play in a league, all the games are played on the same day at the same time. Questions are supplied in a sealed envelope to be opened by the question master in the presence of both teams at the beginning of the match. The questions and answers are normally listed together on a single sheet which is only seen by the question master. We have separated them in the book so that a team member can read out the questions, if necessary, when you are playing at home.

TEAMS
Each team consists of four playing members. In addition, a question master/timekeeper is provided by the home team, and both teams supply a scorer (or the team captains can keep score).

RULES
The match is played in two halves. The question master tosses a coin to see who plays first.

The first four rounds in each half are team rounds. There are five questions for each team, which are asked to each team alternately. Conferring is allowed. If the team cannot answer, or answers incorrectly, the question is passed over to the other team for a bonus.

The final round in each half is a round of individual questions. The team which answers first, answers the individual questions in the first half, and the opposing team answers the individual questions in the second half. At the beginning of the match, each team member chooses his or her subject for the individual round from the five categories provided. Conferring is not allowed on these questions. If they cannot answer the questions, or answer incorrectly, the questions can be passed over to the other team for a bonus, and the opposing team can confer.

All answers to the team questions and to bonus questions must be given by the team captains.

TIMING
Thirty seconds is allowed for each answer, which starts after the question has been read out. An additional 15 seconds is allowed if the question is passed over for a bonus.

SCORING
All correct team questions: 2 points
All correct individual questions: 3 points
All correct bonus questions: 1 point

The question master acts as the adjudicator and his/her decision is final. If they make a mistake which would result in a question being unfair, they can replace it with one of the reserve questions provided.

Teams use the score sheets provided to keep scores. The scorers check and agree the points after each round. You can copy the score sheet provided for home use.

THE DRINKS ROUND
Questions are also provided for a drinks round. These are not counted as part of the match, but can be used as reserve questions if necessary. There are ten questions for each team, which are asked alternately.

Pub League Quiz Score Sheet

1st HALF	HOME		AWAY	
ROUND 1	SCORE	BONUS	SCORE	BONUS
Q1				
Q2				
Q3				
Q4				
Q5				
TOTAL				
ROUND 2				
Q1				
Q2				
Q3				
Q4				
Q5				
TOTAL				
ROUND 3				
Q1				
Q2				
Q3				
Q4				
Q5				
TOTAL				
ROUND 4				
Q1				
Q2				
Q3				
Q4				
Q5				
TOTAL				
ROUND 5				
Q1				
Q2				
Q3				
Q4				
Q5				
TOTAL				
1st HALF	HOME		AWAY	
TOTAL				

FINAL SCORE: _____ *Home Team* _____ *Away Team* _____

2nd HALF	HOME		AWAY	
ROUND 6	SCORE	BONUS	SCORE	BONUS
Q1				
Q2				
Q3				
Q4				
Q5				
TOTAL				
ROUND 7				
Q1				
Q2				
Q3				
Q4				
Q5				
TOTAL				
ROUND 8				
Q1				
Q2				
Q3				
Q4				
Q5				
TOTAL				
ROUND 9				
Q1				
Q2				
Q3				
Q4				
Q5				
TOTAL				
ROUND 10				
Q1				
Q2				
Q3				
Q4				
Q5				
TOTAL				
2nd HALF	HOME		AWAY	
TOTAL				

Pub League Quiz 1

The individual questions are in Rounds 5 and 10 and are on the following subjects: Films, Sport, Science, Pot luck and Geography.

Team 1

Team 2

ROUND 1

1 Who led the Ra expeditions?

2 Who, in 1875, composed the *Symphonie Espagnole*?

3 In which continent would you find the Apennines?

4 Who wrote the poem 'The Lady of the Lake'?

5 Whom did the Jacobites support?

1 What was the purpose of the Ra expeditions?

2 Who wrote the opera *Carmen*?

3 In which continent would you find the Atlas Mountains?

4 Who wrote the poem 'The Lady of Shalott'?

5 Who was the father of James II?

ROUND 2

1 What symbol represents the sign of Cancer in the zodiac?

2 What was Britain's first winning entry in the Eurovision Song Contest?

3 What is the largest living antelope?

4 Which castle is the home of the Dukes of Argyll?

5 To which royal house did George II belong?

1 What zodiac sign is represented by a goat?

2 On which writer's books was the TV series *The Darling Buds of May* based?

3 What type of animal is a lamprey?

4 Where in England is Barnard Castle?

5 Who was the wife of François II of France?

ROUND 3

1 What is RADAR short for?

1 What did OAS stand for?

2 Which is the fourth planet from the sun?

3 Which US chemist discovered nylon?

4 What does the legal term *de jure* mean?

5 Who had his first No. 1 hit as a solo singer two years after his death with 'Living On My Own'?

2 Which is the second planet from the sun?

3 Who in 1837 invented the steel plough?

4 In which year was legal aid introduced in the UK?

5 From which album did Michael Jackson take his hit single 'Black or White'?

ROUND 4

1 Who was the world's first woman prime minister?

2 What is the common name for the clavicle?

3 Which jockey rode Grundy to win the Derby in 1975?

4 Which Canadian city used to be called Bytown?

5 Who wrote *The Cruel Sea*?

1 Who murdered Jean-Paul Marat?

2 Where would you find your deltoid muscle?

3 Which US swimmer won four gold medals in the 1976 Olympics, all in world record times?

4 Which city in Australia took its name from William IV's wife?

5 Who wrote *Utopia*?

ROUND 5   *Individual questions for team 1*

Films
On which classical work was the film *Kiss Me Kate* based?

Sport
Who in baseball was the 'Georgia Peach'?

Science
What is described by c in scientific texts and was considered by Einstein to be the only absolute in the universe?

Pot luck
What is the male singing voice next above baritone?

Geography
What is the tundra?

Team 2

ROUND 6
1 What substance makes plants green?
2 What type of fish is a char?
3 Who wrote *An American Dream*?
4 Which Irish political party was founded in 1933 as a successor to the party led by William Cosgrave?
5 Who is the patron saint of sailors?

ROUND 7
1 What relation was Queen Victoria to George III?
2 Which member of the Rolling Stones drowned in a swimming pool?
3 How many square yards to an acre?
4 Who invented the lightning rod?
5 Who played Bluebottle in *The Goon Show*?

ROUND 8
1 Whose novels are set in the Potteries?
2 What type of animal is a loon?
3 Who composed the opera *Don Giovanni*?
4 Whose vital statistics were 19-19-19?

Team 1

1 What is another name for tungsten?
2 What is a male pike called?
3 Who wrote *A Small Town in Germany*?
4 When was the first National Insurance Act passed in Great Britain?

5 Who is the patron saint of France?

1 What relation was Louis XV of France to Louis XIV?
2 Which composer died of typhoid fever, aged 31?
3 How many acres to a square mile?
4 Who invented the power-loom?
5 Who played Seagoon in *The Goon Show*?

1 Whose novels are set in Wessex?
2 What type of animal is a lumpsucker?
3 How many operas make up the *Ring* cycle of Wagner?
4 Who in fiction owned the dog Gnasher?

5 How many 'pillars of
Islam' are there?

5 What name is given to
the trinity of Hindu gods,
Brahma, Siva and
Vishnu?

ROUND 9
1 Who composed the
music for the ballet
Giselle?
2 What is the name of the
place where Jesus was
crucified?
3 Which famous comedian
sent his Christmas cards
in July?
4 Who in the 1830s and
1840s was nicknamed the
'Factory King'?
5 Who was the Greek
herald who could shout
as loudly as 50 ordinary
men?

1 From which piece of
music does 'Fingal's
Cave' come?
2 What is the name of the
place where Jesus was
arrested?
3 What was W.C. Fields'
real name?
4 Who was the leader of
the Peasants' Revolt?
5 Who in Arthurian legend
found the Holy Grail?

ROUND 10   *Individual questions for team 2*
Films
Who portrayed the US showman George M. Cohan on film?
Sport
Which American tennis player was nicknamed 'Little Mo'?
Science
Samuel Hahnemann is generally credited with the founding
of which medical science?
Pot luck
Name the curate who wrote the classic *Natural History and
Antiquities of Selborne,* published in 1789.
Geography
What sea in the Atlantic Ocean doesn't have a coast?

11

Team 1	Team 2

DRINKS ROUND

1 Who wrote a story about Melibee?

1 Who wrote *Moby Dick*?

2 What does RAPC stand for?

2 What does RLC stand for?

3 What is the capital of the Philippines?

3 What is the capital of Venezuela?

4 What type of fruit is a nectarine?

4 What is the common name of the fruit *Citrus sinensis*?

5 Which great Florentine painter is known by his Christian name rather than his surname, Buonaroti?

5 Which great painter, born Michelangelo Merisi, took the name of the small town in northern Italy where he grew up?

6 In which post-war year was the Morris Minor produced?

6 Who designed the Kodak camera?

7 Who recorded the song 'Think' in 1968?

7 Who recorded the song 'Man of the World' in 1969?

8 How many countries were originally in the EC?

8 Name four of the original EC countries.

9 In computer terminology, what does RAM stand for?

9 In computer terminology, what does ROM stand for?

10 What is the other common name given to the plant delphinium?

10 What is the other name for the plant Nicotiana?

RESERVE QUESTIONS

1 Which fictional detective first appeared in 1920 in *The Mysterious Affair at Styles*?

2 What was the name of the island prison in San Francisco Bay?

3 Which American sprinter, an Olympic gold medallist in 1904 and 1906, was nicknamed the 'Milwaukee Meteor'?

Pub League Quiz 2

The individual questions are in Rounds 5 and 10 and are on the following subjects: Films, The arts, Paris, Who said? and World leaders.

Team 1 | *Team 2*

ROUND 1

Team 1
1 In heraldry, what colour is murrey?
2 What musical instrument would you associate with Reginald Dixon?
3 What is the monetary unit of Senegal?
4 What three colours make up the flag of Iran?
5 Which stretch of water lies between the Bosphorus and the Dardanelles?

Team 2
1 In heraldry, what colour is vert?
2 What musical instrument would you associate with Harry James?
3 What is the monetary unit of Guatemala?
4 What three colours along with three green stars in the centre make up the flag of Iraq?
5 In which country is Ravenna?

ROUND 2

Team 1
1 What historic event took place at Runnymede?
2 What is a glockenspiel?
3 What is measured on the Beaufort Scale?
4 How many paintings did Van Gogh sell during his lifetime?
5 Who wrote *For Whom the Bell Tolls?*

Team 2
1 Where was Napoleon's final place of exile?
2 From where is the word 'bedlam' derived?
3 What is a pitot tube?
4 Which Belgian is famous for the painting *'Ceci n'est pas une pipe'*?
5 Who wrote *Pride and Prejudice*?

ROUND 3

Team 1
1 Which Motown star was killed by his father in 1984?

Team 2
1 Which pop star was knighted in 1995?

2 What was different about the 1970 FA Cup between Leeds United and Chelsea?

3 In which novel by George Eliot does Dr Lydgate appear?

4 What is East Pakistan now known as?

5 Which statesman's slogan was 'You've never had it so good'?

2 Name the white boxer who won the world heavyweight crown by beating Floyd Patterson.

3 Name the Anthony Burgess book about London terrorised by teenage gangs.

4 Monte Marmolada is the highest peak in which mountain range?

5 Which statesman won the Nobel Prize for Literature in 1953?

ROUND 4

1 Who was commander-in-chief of the Spanish Armada?

2 What, according to its advertising slogan, is 'the nation's favourite airline'?

3 Name the lighthouse immediately due west of Land's End.

4 Which prominent member of the New York Dadaists moved to Paris in 1921?

5 In which year did the German forces surrender in Italy?

1 Who commanded the English fleet which defeated the Spanish Armada?

2 What is advertised as 'the bright one, the right one'?

3 Name the lighthouse 23 km south-west of Plymouth.

4 Which Dutch painter's masterpiece is *The Third Marquess of Hamilton*?

5 Where did Field Marshal von Paulus surrender to the Russians in February 1943?

ROUND 5   *Individual questions for team 1*

Films
Who won Best Actress Oscars for her performances in *To Each His Own* (1946) and *The Heiress* (1949)?

The arts
In 1913 Diaghilev's *Ballet Russe* performed a work at the Théatre des Champs Elysées in Paris, which caused a riot. What was the work and who wrote it?

Paris
Which is the oldest bridge over the Seine in Paris?

Who said?
Who promised to 'make Britain a fit place for heroes to live in'?

World leaders
John F. Kennedy was the 35th president of the United States. What did the 'F' represent?

Team 2

Team 1

ROUND 6

1 Who were Gog and Magog?

2 What does the musical term *largo* mean?

3 From which tower of the Palace of Westminster does the Union Jack fly by day when Parliament is sitting?

4 What was printed for the first time in 1455?

5 Through which country does the River Flinders flow?

1 Who slew Grendel and Grendel's mother?

2 What musical instruction means to be played in a sustained or prolonged manner?

3 In which English town would you find the Holst Birthplace Museum?

4 How many books of John are there in the New Testament?

5 In which country does the River Po flow?

15

ROUND 7

1 Which country's civil aircraft markings are OY?
2 Who wrote the poem which begins, 'When I consider how my light is spent'?
3 In which country is Mount Logan?
4 What is '20' in German?
5 Of which country was Jomo Kenyatta president?

1 Which country's civil aircraft have TF markings?
2 Which poem has the first lines, 'Not a drum was heard, not a funeral note'?
3 In which American state is the Great Salt Lake?
4 What is 'eight' in Italian?
5 Of which country was James K. Polk president?

ROUND 8

1 In law, what are the rights of estovers?
2 What did Christian Friedrich Schönbein discover?
3 Who played Emma Peel in *The Avengers*?
4 What is a gazebo?
5 What does RCVS stand for?

1 In law, what is a wayleave?
2 What did Nicholas-Louis Vauquelin discover?
3 Who played Cathy Gale in *The Avengers*?
4 What is the architectural term for a bell-tower?
5 What does EFTA stand for?

ROUND 9

1 Of which disease did D.H. Lawrence die in 1930?
2 Who crowned Napoleon Bonaparte Emperor of the French?
3 Who or what would compete in the Golden Jacket?

1 How did Lawrence of Arabia die?
2 Which emperor's horse was called Bucephalus?
3 Why can a horse not win the Derby in successive years?

4 Give another name for the Tonga Islands.

5 *Pica pica* is another name for which bird?

4 Name the island separated from the mainland by the Juan de Fuca, Georgia and Queen Charlotte Straits.

5 What is a ha-ha?

ROUND 10   *Individual questions for team 2*

Films
Who played Abraham Lincoln in the 1940 film *Abe Lincoln in Illinois*?

The arts
What were the three favourite subjects of the artist Degas?

Paris
Where in Paris is the basilica of Sacré Coeur?

Who said?
Who described Russian policy as 'a riddle wrapped in a mystery inside an enigma'?

World leaders
Who was elected president of Cyprus in 1959?

Team 1
_____

Team 2
_____

DRINKS ROUND

1 What did the owl and the pussy cat take to sea with them?

2 In which Shakespeare play is the famous line, 'Woman, thy name is frailty'?

1 Solomon Grundy, born on Monday, christened on Tuesday, what did he do on Wednesday?

2 Which Dickens character repeatedly said, 'We are so very 'umble'?

3 What is the meaning of the Latin phrase *deo volente*?

4 In which art gallery is the Venus de Milo?

5 What is the name of the Islamic holy month?

6 In which country was Che Guevara born?

7 Which former head of state was found guilty of drugs offences in a US court in 1992?

8 What is a pelerine?

9 What instrument did jazz musician Stan Getz play?

10 Who played Clegg, the former Co-op assistant in *Last of the Summer Wine*?

3 What is the meaning of the Latin phrase *compos mentis*?

4 Where in Belgium is the former house of the painter Rubens?

5 What is the name given to the final battle between God and Satan that is foretold in the Bible?

6 From what country did Cleopatra's ancestors come?

7 Name the Swedish prime minister who was assassinated in 1986.

8 What is a toque?

9 Who in jazz was nicknamed 'Bird'?

10 Who was 'a man called Ironside' on TV?

RESERVE QUESTIONS
1 Name the explorer born in 1728 at Marton-in-Cleveland who charted Australia's east coast?
2 What is the name for the point on the surface of the earth from which the shockwaves of an earthquake proceed?
3 Who was the British prime minister in the reign of Edward VIII?

Pub League Quiz 3

The individual questions are in Rounds 5 and 10 and are on the following subjects: Pot luck, History, Politics, Biology and Art.

Team 1

Team 2

ROUND 1

1 Who wrote the song 'White Christmas'?

2 Scurvy is caused by a deficiency of which vitamin?

3 Why is a white elephant so called?

4 When, legally, is 'time immemorial'?

5 Who was the British prime minister when India was granted independence?

1 Who wrote the song 'Do They Know It's Christmas'?

2 Which letter is at the left of the top row of a typewriter keyboard?

3 Where would you find firedamp?

4 Within what period must a victim's death occur for the crime to be murder?

5 Who became leader of the British Labour Party in 1955?

ROUND 2

1 What kind of creature is a taipan?

2 What do the letters FRGS stand for?

3 Where in Britain is the Martyrs' Memorial to Cranmer, Ridley and Latimer?

4 Who painted *The Fighting Téméraire*?

5 Within 20 ft, how tall is the Blackpool Tower?

1 What breed of dog has the same name as a mythological creature with the head and wings of an eagle and the body of a lion?

2 What do the letters NUS stand for?

3 Where in Britain is Cabot Tower?

4 Who sculpted *Eros* in Piccadilly?

5 Within 30 ft, how tall is the Eiffel Tower?

ROUND 3

1 In which country is the city of Delft?

1 Which town in Spain was noted for its sword blades?

2 In which year was the first women's marathon run in the Olympics?

2 In which sport would you use the term 'catching a crab'?

3 What does a speleologist study?

3 What is a *locum tenens*?

4 Which country's international car registration letters are SF?

4 Which country's international car registration letters are PL?

5 Who discovered Tristan da Cunha?

5 Who discovered Spitsbergen?

ROUND 4

1 Where was the first football World Cup held?

1 Who won the first football World Cup?

2 Which English monarch was killed while out hunting in the New Forest?

2 Which ancient body controls the grazing rights in the New Forest?

3 Who composed the opera *War and Peace*?

3 What nationality was Frederick Delius?

4 In which ocean are the Seychelles?

4 Name the largest of the Seychelle Islands.

5 Who in pop music were Tania Evans and Jay Supreme?

5 Who was successively part of Depeche Mode, Yazoo and Erasure?

ROUND 5   *Individual questions for team 1*

Pot luck
What is a fipple?

History
Which buccaneer was made Lieutenant-Governor of Jamaica in 1674?

Politics
Who led the parliamentary campaign in Britain against the slave trade in the 1800s?

Biology
What is the average heart rate for a normal, healthy human being?

Art
Who was commissioned by the city of Florence to create the sculpture of David?

Team 2 | **Team 1**

ROUND 6

	Team 2		Team 1
1	What is the last word in the New Testament?	1	Name the first three books of the Old Testament.
2	How many pawns are there in a chess game?	2	How many people take part in the Oxford/Cambridge boat race?
3	Name two of Lebanon's three main languages.	3	Name two of Lebanon's three principal religious denominations.
4	Which city did Scot McKenzie sing about?	4	In the Perry Como song, what did Delaware?
5	Which American city is know as 'motor city'?	5	What colour sari is worn by an Indian bride?

ROUND 7

	Team 2		Team 1
1	Which bird is sometimes known as 'Mother Carey's chicken'?	1	Which thrush is also called the storm cock?
2	How many parts of speech are there?	2	Name six of the parts of speech.
3	Which English king was called 'the hammer of the Scots'?	3	Which king of England was nicknamed 'Longshanks'?
4	In which capital city is Hradcany Castle?	4	Where is Shah Jahan's Red Fort?
5	In which sport is the Stanley Cup competed for?	5	In which sport is the Grand Challenge Cup competed for?

ROUND 8

1 Who in a poem by Coleridge decreed a stately pleasure dome in Xanadu?
2 What do the French call the English Channel?
3 What are the Christian names of the heir apparent to the British throne?
4 Which actor played the Fugitive on television?
5 Which metal is alloyed with iron to make stainless steel?

1 Which poem begins, 'He did not wear his scarlet coat'?
2 What is decompression sickness often known as?
3 Where was Princess Elizabeth when her father died in 1952?
4 Who was the Fugitive looking for?
5 From which ore does chromium come?

ROUND 9

1 What is the capital of Bolivia?
2 Who kissed the girls and made them cry?
3 In which country is the volcano Popocatepetl?
4 What monetary unit is used in Afghanistan?
5 In what year did an IRA bomb explode outside Harrods?

1 What is the capital of Trinidad and Tobago?
2 'Ring a Ring of Roses' is about what event?
3 On which island is Fingal's Cave?
4 What monetary unit is used in Iceland?
5 Where were 35 people killed in a crash on the London Underground in 1975?

ROUND 10   *Individual questions for team 2*

Pot luck

The town of Dum-Dum gives its name to a bullet and an airport. To which large city is it close?

History

Which French Jewish soldier was imprisoned on Devil's Island for alleged espionage?

Politics

What was President Tito's original name?

Biology

What name is given to the study of population control by selective breeding?

Art
Vision of a Knight was the work of which Italian painter?

Team 1	Team 2

DRINKS ROUND

Team 1
1 What are the large plains of South America called?

2 Who wrote the novel *The Moonstone*?
3 What is the state capital of Montana?
4 How many laws of motion did Newton propose?
5 What was the name of the B-29 aircraft that dropped the atomic bomb on Hiroshima?
6 In which country is Lund Cathedral?
7 Name the spice that comes from the outer covering of nutmeg.
8 In which country is Rennes?
9 Who was the Philistine giant slain by David?
10 In rugby league, how many points are given for a try?

Team 2
1 Which wind sweeps down from the north along the lower Rhône valley?
2 Who wrote *The Pursuit of Love*?
3 What is the highest peak in the Alps?
4 What kind of acid is normally used in a car battery?
5 Name the last steam locomotive to be built in the UK for express passenger service.
6 In which country is Ulm Cathedral?
7 From what is laver bread made?
8 In which country is Omdurman?
9 What is the music of Rastafarians called?
10 In rugby league, how many points are given for a conversion goal or penalty goal?

RESERVE QUESTIONS
1 From west to east, which countries of the Europe/Asia land mass extend northwards into the Arctic Circle?
2 Where was Archduke Ferdinand assassinated?
3 Name two of the three kinds of artichoke.

Pub League Quiz 4

The individual questions are in Rounds 5 and 10 and are on the following subjects: Kings and queens, Famous men, Sport, Places and General knowledge.

Team 1

ROUND 1

1 Which actor directed the film *The Outlaw Josey Wales*?

2 Who created the Red Indians Chingachgook and Uncas?

3 Name the artificial European language invented by Dr L.L. Zamenhof.

4 What series of races began in 1907 in the Isle of Man?

5 The president of which republic has his office in the Quirinal Palace?

ROUND 2

1 Who, in *The Tempest*, sings to Ferdinand, 'Full fathom five thy father lies'?

2 From which spacecraft was the first moon landing made?

Team 2

1 Which actor directed *Reds*?

2 What was the name of Othello's malignant 'ancient'?

3 Within 30 years, when was Esperanto invented?

4 What does TT stand for?

5 Give another name for the French ministry of foreign affairs derived from the Paris street on which it is situated.

1 What was the name of Hamlet's mother?

2 What was the name of the dog carried into space with Sputnik 2?

3 What name is given to the fruit of the wild rose?

3 Which plant of the same family as the buttercup is also known as 'traveller's joy' and 'old man's beard'?

4. What does FIA stand for?

4 What does FCIB stand for?

5 What type of TV programme was *Gideon's Way*?

5 Which detective thriller had the theme music entitled 'Eye Level'?

ROUND 3

1 What is navarin of lamb?
2 What is the religious denomination of the majority in Germany?
3 Whose last novel was *Endymion*?
4 Who was the first British golfer to win the US Open after the Second World War?
5 Who was sold to Potiphar, an officer of Pharoah and Captain of the Guard?

1 What is a syllabub?
2 What is the religious denomination of the majority in Switzerland?
3 What was Disraeli's first novel called?
4 What animal phrase describes a particularly rough area on a golf course?
5 Name the son of Nun who became leader of the Israelites after the death of Moses.

ROUND 4

1 Whose first British hit was 'Space Oddity'?

2 What new state in the Middle East was proclaimed in 1948?
3 How many sixpences made up half a crown?
4 Name the wizard in the court of the legendary King Arthur.

1 How were the Moody Blues attired at night in a hit record?

2 Which country overthrew its Communist dictator at Christmas in 1989?
3 What is today's value of a florin?
4 What was King Arthur's castle called?

5 What name is given to a geographical index or dictionary?

5 What name is given to the science or study of fungi?

ROUND 5   *Individual questions for team 1*

Kings and queens
Which king was married to Marie-Antoinette?

Famous men
Which American president wrote the book *Profiles in Courage*?

Sport
What colour is the lowest rank judo belt?

Places
For what is the town of Coalport famous?

General knowledge
What were Martello towers originally built for?

Team 2

Team 1

ROUND 6

1 Name one of the planets that shows lunar-type phases as seen from the earth.

1 Name the other planet that shows lunar-type phases as seen from earth.

2 Who wrote the nursery rhyme 'Old Mother Hubbard'?

2 Who wrote *Ivor the Engine*?

3 What is the Norwegian parliament called?

3 Of what university is the Sorbonne a part?

4 Who directed the musical film *Meet Me in St Louis*?

4 Who wrote the musical *Jesus Christ Superstar*?

5 Who wrote the novel *Les Misérables*?

5 Who wrote the novel *Dr Zhivago*?

1   In which country is Monterrey?

2   Which kind of wood was Noah told to use to build his ark?

3   The term ordnance embraces what kind of weapons?

4   Who was the eighteenth-century writer of *The Beggar's Opera*?

5   What was Paddington Bear's country of origin?

1   Which river flows from Colorado to the Gulf of Mexico?

2   What were the manuscripts found in caves at Qumran, Palestine, in 1947 called?

3   Which countries were the British fleet fighting at the Battle of Navarino?

4   *The Septuagint* was the principal Greek version of what?

5   Baroness Orczy wrote about Sir Percy Blakeney. By what other name was Percy Blakeney known?

QUIZ 4

ROUND 8

1   Which poet wrote the line, 'The Paths of Glory lead but to the Grave'?

2   What is the familiar name of the obelisk erected in 1878 on the Victoria Embankment in London?

3   Who played Worzel Gummidge in the television series?

4   Where is the Orange River?

5   What was John Loudon MacAdam's contribution to road transport?

1   Who wrote 'Ode to the West Wind'?

2   Did Eton College receive its first charter in 1240, 1340, 1440, 1540 or 1640?

3   In *Worzel Gummidge*, who played Aunt Sally?

4   In which European country is Mount Ossa?

5   Which well known motor vehicle was launched in 1959 by Alec Issigonis?

ROUND 9

1   What is an animal's pug?
2   Who said, 'England is a nation of shopkeepers'?

3   Which group of instruments are positioned closest to the conductor in an orchestra?

4   Who in the Bible wore a coat of many colours?

5   Of which country was Douglas Hyde president?

1   What is simony?
2   Who wrote, 'If God did not exist it would be necessary to invent him'?

3   What sort of instrument was a flageolet?

4   Who in the Bible was rid of seven demons by Jesus?

5   What nationality was the father of Eamon de Valera?

ROUND 10   *Individual questions for team 2*

Kings and queens
Which king died near Rouen in 1087 and is buried at Caen?

Famous men
How did Ernest Hemingway die?

Sport
In what year did Britain last win an Olympic Gold for football?

Places
In which town is Brunel University?

General knowledge
Who, but for disclaiming the peerage, would be Viscount Stansgate?

Team 1
_____

Team 2
_____

DRINKS ROUND

1   Which saint's day is April 25?

1   Which saint's day is July 25?

2 Which prelate was killed on the orders of Henry II, which Henry said had been misinterpreted?

3 What is the British Army equivalent of the rank of rear-admiral in the Navy?

4 What is the monetary unit of Peru?

5 Who wrote the novel *Le Rouge et le Noir*?

6 Which famous film star was born William Henry Pratt?

7 In which country is the Irrawaddy Delta?

8 How many faces has a prism?

9 Where is Great Slave Lake?

10 Who played Superintendent Tyburn in TV's *Heat of the Sun*?

2 Which Bolshevik leader was killed in Mexico City by a Stalinist agent?

3 What is the naval equivalent of the rank of brigadier in the British Army?

4 What is the monetary unit of Nepal?

5 Who wrote the novel *Cousine Bette*?

6 Who starred in *Spartacus, The Boston Strangler* and *The Last Tycoon*?

7 In which country is the River Test?

8 How many sides has a rhombus?

9 Where is Bala Lake?

10 Who played the narrator in *Brideshead Revisited*?

RESERVE QUESTIONS
1 The Americans call it a tuxedo. What do the British call it?
2 A food that is 'butyraceous' contains or resembles what?
3 What would a sailor do with a scuttlebut?

Pub League Quiz 5

The individual questions are in Rounds 5 and 10 and are on the following subjects: Mythology and legend, Africa, Entertainment, People and places, and Numbers.

Team 1

ROUND 1
1 What type of animal is an ortolan?
2 Which footballer won 108 caps for England and finished his playing career with Fulham?
3 Where do the 'Expos' play baseball?
4 What is the largest of the four provinces of the Republic of Ireland?
5 Whose first book of poems was *A Twin Cloud*?

ROUND 2
1 Who composed oratorios entitled 'St Paul' and 'Elijah'?
2 Which British biologist founded and named the science of genetics?
3 What does FRCS stand for?
4 Which actor played the title role in the 1963 spoof horror film *The Raven*?

Team 2

ROUND 1
1 What predatory animal is also call a prairie wolf?
2 Name the German who was footballer of the year in 1970.
3 What soccer team play at Edgar Street?
4 Name four of the counties that make up Munster.
5 Who wrote *Mr Midshipman Easy*?

ROUND 2
1 At what age did Yehudi Menuhin make his concert debut?
2 At which London teaching hospital did Alexander Fleming discover penicillin?
3 What does FRHS stand for?
4 In which country was Peter Lorre born?

5 Of which river is the River Drava a tributary?

5 In which country does the Rhine rise?

ROUND 3

1 Indigenous covered five furlongs in world record time for the distance at Epsom in 1960. What was his speed: a little over 35 mph, 40 mph, 45 mph or 50 mph?

1 Red Rum recorded the fastest time ever for the Grand National in 1973. Was his time a little over seven, eight, nine or 10 minutes?

2 Who sang 'Help Me Make It Through the Night' in 1972?

2 Who sang 'Autumn Almanac' in 1967?

3 Which comedian was christened Eric Bartholomew?

3 Who, according to Benny Hill, 'drove the fastest milk cart in the West'?

4 A very large armadillo is called a 'giant'. What is the smallest type of armadillo called?

4 Of which continent is the aardvark a native?

5 By what name is Peter Sutcliffe better known?

5 Which African leader gave himself the title 'Conqueror of the British Empire'?

ROUND 4

1 Which mollusc protects itself by ejecting a cloud of inky fluid called sepia?

1 How many tentacles has a cuttlefish?

2 Whose assassination in 1924 led to anti-Fascist demonstrations in the Italian parliament?

2 What position did Hendrik Verwoerd hold at the time of his assassination?

3 What were the several thousand projectiles used in Laurel and Hardy's *Battle of the Century*?

3 Who was reputed to be the fastest mouse in all of Mexico?

4 Which Roman emperor instigated the second invasion of England?

5 Who played Basil Fawlty on TV?

4 In whose reign was the 'Wonderful Parliament' of 1388?

5 Who played Sybil Fawlty on TV?

ROUND 5   *Individual questions for team 1*

Mythology and legend
Whose temple was the Parthenon?

Africa
Which country lies between Ghana and Benin?

Entertainment
Which famous dance hall was opened in Paris in 1900?

People and places
Where was the Minoan civilisation?

Numbers
Divide £66 amongst A, B and C, so that B has £8 more than A, and C £14 more than B.

Team 2

Team 1

ROUND 6

1 Who was the first woman mayor in Britain?

2 Who in music was 'Flash Harry'?

3 What British medal is given for saving life at sea or on land?

4 Who wrote *Cakes and Ale*?

5 Which sign comes after Cancer in the zodiac?

1 Who was the first Archbishop of Canterbury?

2 For what was Emmeline Pankhurst famous?

3 What is the highest military decoration awarded in the USA?

4 Who wrote *Love's Labour's Lost*?

5 Which sign comes after Scorpio in the zodiac?

QUIZ
5

ROUND 7

1 Who said, 'Now I am on the side of the angels'?

1 Who said, 'An army marches on its stomach'?

2 Which Pope reigned from 1958 to 1963?

2 Who in the twentieth century was Pope for only 33 days?

3 Name the mountain range in County Down, Northern Ireland.

3 Name the highest peak in Northern Ireland.

4 From which album did George Michael take four No. 1 hits?

4 Who had a hit album called *Gracelands*?

5 What is a gravimeter?

5 What is a magnetometer?

QUIZ
5

ROUND 8

1 Which European country claims to have the oldest parliament?

1 What nationality were Karl Marx and Friedrich Engels?

2 Which is the brightest of the five planets visible to the naked eye?

2 Which is the hottest of the planets in the solar system?

3 Which writer created the Toff?

3 Which writer created Father Brown?

4 Which actress starred as Julie in the film *Showboat* in 1951?

4 Which actress's story was portrayed in the 1981 film *Mommie Dearest*?

5 What is a perfect score in a gymnastics exercise?

5 What is the hop, step and jump officially called?

ROUND 9

1 In which county is the New Forest?

1 The Forest of Dean is almost wholly in one county; which county is this?

2 The Queen's Cup and the Prince Philip Cup are competed for in which sport?

3 Who in the Bible was famous for his wisdom?

4 Who composed the music for the film *High Society*?

5 Who was the chief commentator for the BBC on the coronation of Elizabeth II?

2 The King George V Gold Cup and the Queen Elizabeth II Cup are competed for in which sport?

3 According to Exodus, what was the first commandment?

4 What is the American equivalent to the British music hall?

5 What were the names of the three radio programmes before Radios 1, 2, 3 and 4?

ROUND 10   *Individual questions for team 2*

Mythology and legend
What is another name for the Roman god Amor?

Africa
In which country is Timbuktu?

Entertainment
Who played the green monster in *The Incredible Hulk*?

People and places
For what is George Horace Gallup remembered?

Numbers
Divide the number 16 into two, so that the sum of the squares of the two parts is 130.

Team 1

Team 2

DRINKS ROUND

1 What is a steak called that has been cut from between two ribs?

1 What is the main ingredient of taramasalata?

2 Who is buried in some corner of a foreign field that is for ever England?

3 What is the simplest compound of hydrogen and oxygen?

4 Who was the Oscar-winning star in the 1939 film of *Goodbye Mr Chips*?

5 What colour is the gemstone malachite?

6 How long did Jonah spend inside the whale?

7 Who wrote the play *Cat on a Hot Tin Roof*?

8 Which cartoonist created the character Maudie Littlehampton?

9 In which year did Samuel Pepys begin his famous diary?

10 Name the character who sucks his thumb in the strip cartoon *Peanuts*.

2 The word 'cenotaph' comes from two Greek words. What does it actually mean?

3 What gas is most plentiful in the air that we breathe?

4 Who was the Oscar-winning star of the films *Gaslight* and *Anastasia*?

5 What colour is the gemstone citrine?

6 Who was Herodias's famous daughter?

7 Who wrote *The Corn is Green*?

8 Name the cartoonist who drew absurdly complicated and fantastic machines.

9 In which year were the lions added to the foot of Nelson's Column?

10 Name Mickey Mouse's girlfriend.

QUIZ 5

RESERVE QUESTIONS
1 What is an amadavat?
2 St Andrew is the patron saint of which country other than Scotland?
3 What is the capital of New York State?

Pub League Quiz 6

The individual questions are in Rounds 5 and 10 and are on the following subjects: Classical music, Motoring, History, Television and Chance.

Team 1

ROUND 1
1 What is a tazza?
2 Who said, 'Genius is one per cent inspiration and 99 per cent perspiration'?
3 Which of these composers set the story of Romeo and Juliet to music? Tchaikovsky, Prokofiev, Berlioz, Bernstein?
4 Who wrote *Up the Junction*?
5 Who became prime minister as MP for Sedgefield?

ROUND 2
1 Which drug is obtained from the cinchona tree?
2 What was the former name of Thailand?
3 What do the Jewish people call the day of atonement?
4 Who twice succeeded Ramsay MacDonald as British prime minister?

Team 2

1 What is a megalith?
2 Who said, 'War is much too serious a thing to be left to the military'?
3 Which Verdi opera is based on Shakespeare's *The Merry Wives of Windsor*?
4 Who wrote *The Jewel in the Crown*?
5 What title did Margaret Thatcher take in the House of Lords?

1 What is novocaine widely used as?
2 What is an inhabitant of Oxford called?
3 What is a bar mitzvah?
4 Who succeeded F.D. Roosevelt as American president?

5   What is a spectrograph?

5   What is a heliograph?

ROUND 3

1   Which mountains form the boundary between European Russia and Siberia?

1   Give another name for the River Hwango-Ho.

2   Which Scottish football team plays at Hampden Park?

2   How long is a cricket pitch from stumps to stumps?

3   In Mecca, what is the name of the Holy of Holies?

3   Diwali, or Festival of Light, is an important celebration in which religion?

4   What does NAAFI stand for?

4   What does ISBN stand for?

5   Who played King Arthur in the film *Camelot*?

5   Who played the Wicked Lady in the 1945 version of the film of the same name?

ROUND 4

1   Which monarch was the son of Henry VIII and Jane Seymour?

1   How many complaints did Luther list and nail on the church door at Wittenberg?

2   By what name is the figure, design or device FYLFOT better known?

2   A bundle of rods tied with an axe in the middle, was the emblem of which political movement?

3   Who wrote, 'O my luve's like a red, red rose that's newly sprung in June'?

3   Who wrote, 'Laugh, and the world laughs with you; weep, and you weep alone'?

4   Who said, 'The only thing I mind about going to prison is the thought of Lord Longford coming to visit me'?

4   Who said, 'Those in the cheap seats clap, the rest of you rattle your jewellery'?

5 Which film studio had a roaring lion as its trade mark?

5 Which film studio had a radio station mast as its trade mark?

ROUND 5   *Individual questions for team 1*

Classical music
The *Symphonie Fantastique* is a popular work by which French composer?

Motoring
When was the AA founded?

History
Who shot the British prime minister Spencer Perceval?

Television
Which TV programme opened with a naked light bulb swinging to and fro?

Chance
Which two countries are separated by the Palk Strait?

Team 2

Team 1

ROUND 6

1 In which country is the Murray River?
2 Whose only novel was *Gone with the Wind*?

3 What do the Muslims call their god?

4 What does FRSL stand for?
5 Name the dry brown brandy distilled in the French district of Gers.

1 In which American state is the Mojave Desert?
2 Whose first successful novel was entitled *Decline and Fall*?
3 What did Salome receive as a reward from Herod for her dancing?
4 What does NOIC stand for?
5 If you saw 'fino' on a bottle, what would you expect to find in it?

ROUND 7

1 Off the coast of which country was the Second World War Battle of Matapan?

2 What sport's name means literally 'empty hand'?

3 What is nephology the study of?

4 'Much have I travell'd in the realms of gold', is the opening line of a poem by whom?

5 Who was the last twentieth-century prime minister educated at Eton?

1 Who commanded the British fleet at the Battle of the Nile?

2 What sport's name means literally 'gentle way'?

3 What is the opposite of Utopia?

4 'Earth has not anything to show more fair', is the opening line of a poem by whom?

5 Who was the conductor at the opening of the Carnegie Hall, New York?

ROUND 8

1 Which famous character was created by Richard Herne?

2 Which building in London is associated with looking after English lighthouses?

3 For which sport is the town of Klosters famous?

4 What German word, often used in art criticism, means 'work in bad taste'?

1 Name two of the Beatles' five films.

2 Where is HMS *Victory* moored?

3 Where is a mountain called Kosciusko?

4 By what name was Anna Robertson, the US painter, better known?

5 Who had a historic meeting in Ujiji in 1871?

5 Which two fictional characters met supposedly for the last time on a precipice over the Reichenbach Falls?

ROUND 9

1 What name is given to the stem of a plant from which the leaves, buds and side shoots spring?

1 What name is given to a plant's main root?

2 Who played Stewart McMillan in *McMillan and Wife*?

2 Who played the Charmer on TV?

3 What is the medical term for the back part of the neck?

3 What is the more usual name for coryza?

4 What do the letters DC mean, as in Washington DC?

4 What does AWACS stand for?

5 Which burglar, hanged in 1879, carried his tools in a violin case?

5 To which piece of clothing did Sir Anthony Eden give his name?

ROUND 10   *Individual questions for team 2*

Classical music
Who composed 'The Creation' and 'The Seasons'?

Motoring
What major contribution to motoring did Percy Shaw make?

History
Which wife of Henry VIII was the mother of Queen Elizabeth I?

Television
What programme has appeared since 1956 on three different channels and provides a review of recent events in the light of newspaper coverage?

Chance
What do the letters MS after a doctor's name mean?

Team 1	Team 2

DRINKS ROUND

1 Gerardus Mercator was famous for what skill?

2 The 'Yom Kippur War' is also known as the 'Six-Day War'. Is that true or false?

3 In Greek mythology who were the twins who were turned into stars?

4 What is the white ring on an archery target called?

5 With which sport would you associate Babe Ruth?

6 What theory starts with the formula $e = mc^2$?

7 Who wrote *The Hunchback of Notre Dame*?

8 What is a palomino?

9 In computer terminology what does GIGO mean?

10 Which is the largest of the Inner Hebrides?

1 Queen Salote reigned over which island kingdom?

2 The Duchess of Windsor was married three times. Is this true or false?

3 What is the connection between the Greek mythological character Procrustes and a bed?

4 What is the central division on a backgammon board called?

5 With which sport would you associate the Jules Rimet Cup?

6 Who developed the Special Theory of Relativity?

7 Who wrote *The Road Past Mandalay*?

8 What is a motmot?

9 What chemical element has the symbol Sb?

10 What is Scotland's longest loch?

QUIZ
6

RESERVE QUESTIONS

1 Who created Colonel Blimp?

2 In which city did the St Valentine's Day Massacre take place in 1929?

3 Who recorded 'Like a Virgin' in 1984?

Pub League Quiz 7

The individual questions are in Rounds 5 and 10 and are on the following subjects: Holiday and travel, Food and drink, Music, The Bible and History.

Team 1

ROUND 1

1 Who succeeded Charles de Gaulle as French president in 1969?
2 Who wrote *The Napoleon of Notting Hill*?
3 What is the SI unit of time?
4 Who wrote the music for 'Rule, Britannia'?

5 How many times did Rod Laver win the men's singles at Wimbledon?

ROUND 2

1 What is Greek for the letter 'K'?
2 Who sculpted *The Thinker* and *The Kiss*?

Team 2

1 Which British prime minister was born in Canada in 1858?
2 Which dramatist invented the character of Mrs Malaprop?
3 What was once known as brimstone?
4 Who wrote the anthem 'Zadok the Priest', performed at all British coronations since that of George II?
5 In which athletics event was Dick Fosbury an Olympic record holder?

1 What is the fourth letter of the Greek alphabet?
2 With what kind of paintings do you associate with the names of Nicholas Hilliard, Richard Cosway and George Engleheart?

3 Which mob was led by Alec Guinness?

4 In which country is Cape Trafalgar?

5 Which rock did Sir George Rooke take for Queen Anne in 1704?

3 Who played Napoleon in the 1970 film of *Waterloo*?

4 On which river does Ottawa stand?

5 Who was the seventeenth-century adventurer who almost succeeded in stealing the crown jewels?

ROUND 3

1 What does WCC stand for?

2 Who wrote the novel *Brighton Rock*?

3 What is the country of origin of the Proton motor car?

4 Which branch of mathematics takes its name from the Latin word for pebble?

5 Who wrote the music for *Kiss Me Kate*?

1 What does CBI stand for?

2 Who wrote *The Green Hills of Africa*?

3 Which motor manufacturer made the Plus 4, Plus 8 and SS models?

4 How did the word 'salary' originate?

5 Who wrote the music for the operetta *Showboat*?

ROUND 4

1 What kind of animal is an eider?

2 When in the church calendar is Advent?

3 Who designed the Horse Guards building in Whitehall and the Royal Mews?

4 Which famous film was based on the life of William Randolph Hearst?

1 What kind of animal is a gecko?

2 What is the literal meaning of 'Advent'?

3 Who designed Regent's Park, Regent Street and the Royal Pavilion, Brighton?

4 What was captured in the film *The Taking of Pelham 123*?

5 In which ocean would you find Ascension Island?

5 In which ocean would you find Ashmore Reef and Cartier Island?

ROUND 5 *Individual questions for team 1*

Holiday and travel
If you were on Mona, where would you be?

Food and drink
What name is given to the thin type of pancake eaten throughout Mexico?

Music
Which composer would you associate with the Brandenburg Concertos?

The Bible
Who were the parents of John the Baptist?

History
What relation was King Haakon VII of Norway to King Edward VII of Britain?

Team 2

Team 1

ROUND 6
1 What is marl a mixture of?
2 Which organ produces insulin?
3 What sporting event did Dionicio Ceron of Mexico win in April 1995?
4 Which family lives at Emmerdale Farm?
5 What name is given to a bishop's head-dress?

1 From which ore is aluminium extracted?
2 Which organ is concerned with balance?
3 Ellery Hanley was captain of which Rugby League team?
4 In *Eastenders* who got Michelle pregnant?
5 What is the skirt-like garment worn by Malaysians called?

ROUND 7

1 What is an *infanta*?
2 What is the capital of Pakistan?
3 Who wrote *Women in Love*?

4 What RNVR stand for?

5 Who was the British chancellor of the exchequer from 1974–79?

1 What is a *mazurka*?
2 What is the capital of Nova Scotia?
3 What did the D.H. in D.H. Lawrence stand for?

4 What does RCMP stand for?

5 Who was the British prime minister from 1970–74?

ROUND 8

1 What type of tree is the lemon tree?
2 Which battle was fought on 21 October 1805?

3 Who was the oldest holder of the world heavyweight boxing crown?
4 In a suit of medieval armour what part of the body is covered by greaves?
5 On which river is Winchester?

1 Give another name for the wellingtonia.
2 The Jacobites were defeated in 1746. At which battle?

QUIZ 7

3 Who was the lightest world heavyweight boxing champion ever?

4 What was Louis IX the last to lead?

5 The confluence of which two rivers forms the Humber?

ROUND 9

1 Which country has the international vehicle registration letter CH?
2 Who summoned the 'Model Parliament'?

1 What is the international vehicle registration letter for Germany?
2 Which famous battle took place in July 1690?

45

3 What do football, Woolworth, Heinz and Dr Pepper have in common?

4 To which subsequent poet laureate was Sylvia Plath married?

5 In which country is the city of Chihuahua?

3 How many cards are there in a Tarot pack with the Greater and Lesser Arcana?

4 Which poet laureate declared, 'I must go down to the seas again, to the lonely sea and the sky'?

5 In which countries is the region of Patagonia?

ROUND 10 *Individual questions for team 2*

Holiday and travel
Who exactly requests and requires free passage for the bearer of a British passport?

Food and drink
What are Desirées, Majestics and Vanessas?

Music
Which composer's sixth symphony is known as the 'Pastoral'?

The Bible
What did Solomon begin to build 'in the second day of the second month, in the fourth year of his reign'?

History
Who was the Confederate president at the time of the American Civil War?

Team 1

Team 2

DRINKS ROUND

1 What is the former name of Malawi?

2 Which fictional character did Reg Smythe create?

1 Which country has the Malabar Coast?

2 Whose arch enemy is Ming the Merciless?

3 What organisation, formed in 1863, has its headquarters in Geneva?

4 What liqueur is made from high-proof brandy, wormwood and other aromatics?

5 Who choreographed the musical *42nd Street*?

6 Name one of the official languages of Afghanistan.

7 Which writer and peer bought London's Playhouse Theatre in 1992?

8 What is the capital of Uruguay?

9 Name the year that Idi Amin ordered the expulsion of British Asians from Uganda, Maurice Chevalier died and Sir John Betjeman became Poet Laureate.

10 Who starred in the silent western *Destry Rides Again*?

3 By what name is the equivalent of the Red Cross known in Muslim countries?

4 What liqueur is made from Dalmation cherries?

5 Who co-directed and starred in the film *Singing in the Rain*?

6 Which country's language has two major dialects, Gheg and Tosk?

7 Who succeeded Sir Peter Hall as director of the National Theatre?

8 What is the capital of Mongolia?

9 Name the year breakfast TV began in Britain, the Franks Report on the Falklands was published and Derby winner Shergar was stolen.

10 Who wrote the story *Destry Rides Again*?

RESERVE QUESTIONS
1 The Melling Road crosses which racecourse?
2 How many eyes has the wolf spider?
3 Which Scottish chemist perpetuated his name with an invention of a waterproof fabric for garments in 1823?

Pub League Quiz 8

The individual questions are in Rounds 5 and 10 and are on the following subjects: Dress and fashion, Law, Inventors and inventions, Famous men and Words.

Team 1

ROUND 1
1 What is the chief port of Iraq?
2 What name is given to animals that eat both vegetable and animal foods?
3 Name Noah's three sons.
4 What type of material is guipure?
5 Who first manufactured basaltes ware crockery?

ROUND 2
1 Name two of the founder members of the United Artists film company.
2 Who defeated Prince Rupert at Marston Moor?
3 Who wrote *Ending Up*?
4 What are igneous rocks?

Team 2

1 Which is the second city and port of Algeria?
2 What name is given to an animal with no backbone?
3 Who was the prostitute who aided Joshua during the siege of Jericho?
4 What in architecture is a lancet?
5 Which potter was the first to produce the famous willow pattern ware in Britain?

1 Which film star's body was stolen by grave robbers in Switzerland?
2 Who was the father of the first Prince of Wales?
3 Who wrote *The Little Match Girl*?
4 What is the geological name for the outer rocky shell of the earth?

5 What is the fat-like substance derived from sheep's wool and used with water as a base for ointments and cosmetics?

5 Name the form of oxygen in which three atoms form one molecule, that is found most abundantly in the upper atmosphere.

ROUND 3

1 Who removed a thorn from a lion's foot and later faced the same lion in a Roman arena?

1 Who constructed the labyrinth for King Minos of Crete?

2 Who was Pearl Bailey?

2 Which jazz composer and saxophonist married Cleo Laine?

3 Where in your body would you find aqueous humour?

3 Where in your body is your olfactory organ?

4 Who was the first black American tennis player to win the Wimbledon men's singles title?

4 How many goals did England score in the 1966 World Cup final?

5 Who wrote the opera *Madame Butterfly*?

5 Which Verdi opera was about the son of Phillip II of Spain?

QUIZ
8

ROUND 4

1 What did Clyde Tombaugh discover?

1 What name is given to a luminous concentration of gas and dust in space?

2 Who had a hit with 'My Guy'?

2 Who in a pop song was 'wearing the face that she keeps in a jar by the door'?

3 Who first patented the phonograph?

3 Who invented the spinning-jenny?

4 What does ECG stand for?

4 What does MRC stand for?

5 Who lived at 23 Railway Cuttings, Cheam?

5 Who played Alf Garnett's daughter in *Till Death Us Do Part*?

ROUND 5   *Individual questions for team 1*

Dress and fashion
Which fashion designer was responsible for the 'New Look'?

Law
What is the name given to the prosecution of a public official by the legislature of the state?

Inventors and inventions
Who invented the vacuum flask?

Famous men
He was born in 1856 and died in 1939. He was Austrian by birth and specialised in psycho-analysis. Who was he?

Words
What is the first meaning of didactic?

Team 2	Team 1

ROUND 6

Team 2	Team 1
1 Excluding Oxford and Cambridge, which is the oldest university in England?	1 Which is the oldest college in the USA?
2 Which fruit is a cross between a grapefruit and a tangerine?	2 Which fruit is a cross between a blackberry and a raspberry?
3 Where is the home of Radio Hallam?	3 Where are the headquarters of Radio Piccadilly?
4 Arthur Koestler wrote a history of cosmology. What is it called?	4 Where was Arthur Koestler born?
5 Where did Nelson lose the sight of his right eye?	5 Where did Nelson lose his right arm?

ROUND 7

1 Who was the king of Iraq who fought against the Turks with T.E. Lawrence in the First World War?

2 Name the two stars of *A Midsummer Night's Sex Comedy*?

3 Who played Hannibal Smith in *The A-Team*?

4 Who wrote *The Honourable Schoolboy*?

5 What was Derek Trotter's nickname in *Only Fools and Horses*?

1 What is the family name of the ruling house of Saudi Arabia?

2 Which actress co-starred with Clint Eastwood in *The Enforcer*?

3 Who played Faceman in *The A-Team*?

4 Who wrote *Lorna Doone*?

5 What was different about Harpo's character?

ROUND 8

1 According to Shakespeare, how many daughters did King Lear have?

2 What are the colours of the flag of the United Nations?

3 The first of the Great Western Railway's main lines was completed in 1841. Between which two cities did it run?

4 Who topped the charts for 10 weeks in 1992 with 'I Will Always Love You'?

5 What type of dog is a Bedlington?

1 What was Mrs Warren's profession in the play by George Bernard Shaw?

2 What is the American national anthem called?

3 Within three years, when was the Stockton and Darlington Railway opened?

4 In which city were Wet Wet Wet formed?

5 Name one of the two main types of Welsh corgi.

QUIZ
8

ROUND 9

1 Which is the largest of the national parks in Great Britain?
2 What is the 'Apple Isle' to Australians?
3 What nationality was Marie-Antoinette?
4 Where in football is the Stretford End?
5 What does MM stand for?

1 Name one of the three people who set up the National Trust.
2 Which is the largest city in Australia?
3 What nationality was Marie Curie?
4 In which sport is a sand-wedge used?
5 What does MLR stand for?

ROUND 10   *Individual questions for team 2*

Dress and fashion
Which French fashion designer was responsible for the 'little black dress'?

Law
What word describes a person who dies without leaving a will?

Inventors and inventions
Who planned a mechanical calculator, the forerunner to the modern computer?

Famous men
Which surgeon first performed the human heart transplant operation?

Words
What is hypermetropia?

Team 1 _____   *Team 2* _____

DRINKS ROUND

1 Who wrote *The Egoist*?

2 What piece of furniture was always featured on *The Val Doonican Show*?

1 Who wrote *The Tailor of Gloucester*?

2 Who was the first presenter of *Tomorrow's World*?

3 What nationality was speedway star Ivan Maugher?

4 What are marlin?

5 Who painted *The Reapers* and *The Gleaners*?

6 What were the female fans of Frank Sinatra called?

7 What is the chemical symbol for mercury?

8 What name is given to second-year students at American universities?

9 What is processed germinated barley called?

10 Name one of the independent kingdoms between India and China.

3 When did women first compete in the Olympics?

4 What is a baby hare called?

5 What is *La Giaconda* better known as?

6 What instrument did King Oliver play?

7 What is the chemical symbol for magnesium?

8 What school of Greek philosophy gave its name to reasoning that is plausible but false?

9 What is sweet corn?

10 What is the old name for the South African province of Kwa Zulu?

QUIZ
8

RESERVE QUESTIONS

1 Charles Wesley was a prodigious writer of hymns. Did he write over 2,500, 3,500, 4,500 or 5,500?

2 Roger Bannister ran the first sub four-minute mile in 1954, by how much less than four minutes?

3 From which fruit is slivovitz made?

Pub League Quiz 9

The individual questions are in Rounds 5 and 10 and are on the following subjects: Water life, Television, Organisations, Games and Flight.

Team 1

Team 2

ROUND 1

Team 1

1 'Empty Garden' was a tribute by Elton John to whom?
2 Where might you find a finial, a chevet and a slype?
3 Who wrote *The Female Eunuch*?
4 Which country was the first to grant women the vote?
5 By what name is K'ung tsu better known?

Team 2

1 Which Dire Straits album became the first million-selling CD?
2 In medieval times where would you have found loopholes?
3 Which novel by Jane Austen was originally called *First Impressions*?
4 Which Middle Ages heroine was born at Domrémy?
5 Which Church of England bishop would sign himself 'Sarum'?

QUIZ
9

ROUND 2

Team 1

1 What colour is the three ball in pool?
2 What does AWOL stand for?
3 What made the Lascaux Cave in south-west France famous?

Team 2

1 In croquet singles, what other colour ball does the player with blue have?
2 What do Mc and Mac mean in surnames?
3 Which modern animal is descended from the eohippus?

4 Which enemy of Batman usually carries an umbrella?

5 Which Washington edifice has 898 steps?

ROUND 3

1 In which country was Maria Bueno born?

2 On the London Underground map what colour represents the Bakerloo Line?

3 In which country did Antony and Cleopatra end their lives?

4 What was the code name for the German invasion of Russia?

5 Which actress played Judy opposite James Dean's Jim in *Rebel Without a Cause*?

ROUND 4

1 Which Caribbean island was invaded by US forces in 1983?

2 What is majolica?

3 Which constellation is the water bearer?

4 What is the sequel to D.H. Lawrence's *The Rainbow*?

5 Who was known as 'the flying Finn'?

4 On which planet was Superman born?

5 Which Rome tourist attraction has 137 steps?

1 Who defected at the 1975 American Tennis Open?

2 What is the national, long-distance railroad system in the USA called?

3 Who is Jessica's father in *The Merchant of Venice*?

4 What was the code name for the allied invasion of Normandy?

5 Who played the girl in *The Girl Can't Help It*?

1 Where do you pass through the Pedro Miguel locks?

2 What are grissini?

3 Which star is known as the Dog Star?

4 Who wrote *Ivanhoe*?

5 Which Olympic gold medallist was banned from athletics in 1913 when it was discovered he had played minor league baseball for money?

ROUND 5   *Individual questions for team 1*

Water life
What is an infant whale called?

Television
Which Glasgow comedian is know as 'The Big Yin'?

Organisations
Which organisation works for human rights all over the world?

Games
At what game are points scored 'below the line'?

Flight
Who manufactured the Comet airliner?

Team 2	Team 1

ROUND 6

1   How long did Sleeping Beauty sleep?

1   Who owned a chocolate factory in the film of Roald Dahl's story?

2   Which part did Judy Garland play in the film *The Wizard of Oz*?

2   Who created Kermit the frog?

3   What is Bolivia's chief export?

3   Which country has the world's largest sheep population?

4   What was the nickname of Rolls-Royce's experimental vertical take-off aircraft?

4   What was the nickname of the Model T Ford?

5   Which famous landmark was designed by Auguste Bartholdi?

5   For what event did Gustave Eiffel build the Eiffel Tower?

ROUND 7

1   What class is categorised as the bourgeoisie?

1   What is the only house in England that the Queen may not legally enter?

2 Which musical was based on T.H. White's novel *The Once and Future King*?

3 Which bird is on Australia's coat of arms?

4 What was the name of Edward Heath's yacht?

5 How often is golf's Ryder Cup played?

2 Which musical 'horror' was first staged in 1974?

3 Which famous Sydney landmark was opened in March 1932?

4 Which famous explorer sailed in the *Theodore Roosevelt*?

5 In boxing what weight division comes between heavyweight and light-heavyweight?

ROUND 8

1 The Hawaiian flag carries the flag of which country in its upper left-hand corner?

2 What does UDR stand for?

3 Who was the first woman to fly the Atlantic solo in 1932?

4 Which country is the setting for Edgar Allan Poe's *The Pit and the Pendulum*?

5 What country's flag is red with a white crescent and star?

1 The flag of which nation flies over Easter Island?

2 Which sport's ruling body is the FIBA?

3 Where did Phineas Fogg begin and end his trip around the world?

4 Which English county provided the setting for most of L.S. Lowry's work?

5 What single colour constitutes the flag of Libya?

QUIZ
9

ROUND 9

1 Which liqueur is the base for a Copenhagen Mary?

1 Which spirit was known in eighteenth-century England as Cuckold's Comfort, Make Shift and Ladies' Delight?

2 What was the prequel to *Gentlemen Marry Brunettes*?

3 Which leader was known as the 'Lion of Judah'?

4 What, to the nearest 5 per cent, is the approximate percentage of the world covered by oceans?

5 Which insect transmits yellow fever?

2 Who created Charlie Chan?

3 Who was the only English pope?

4 Where is the Beaufort Sea?

5 What is rubella better known as?

ROUND 10 *Individual questions for team 2*

Water life
Which fish's skin was once commercially used as sandpaper?

Television
Which *Peyton Place* star married Frank Sinatra?

Organisations
What organisation did Pol Pot lead?

Games
How many different colours are the spaces on a Scrabble board?

Flight
Where was London's first airport?

Team 1 _____

Team 2 _____

DRINKS ROUND

1 What was John Steinbeck's travelling companion Charley?

1 Which books tell the stories of Brer Fox and Brer Rabbit?

2 Where did the gunfight at the OK Corral take place?

3 By what Indian name is Mount McKinley also known?

4 What do gall wasps cause in oak trees?

5 Who was the first woman to produce, write, direct and star in a major Hollywood film?

6 In which country is Casablanca?

7 From what game do we get the phrase 'stand pat'?

8 Which is the only female animal that has antlers?

9 Which English artist drew *The Anatomy of the Horse*?

10 In which county would you find the prehistoric monuments of Stonehenge?

2 Which film had gunslinger Frank Miller arriving on the midday train?

3 In which US state is Mount McKinley?

4 Which trees are commonly found in English churchyards?

5 Which of the film title characters played by Charlton Heston was known in real life as Rodrigo Diaz de Vivar?

6 The Owen Falls are below the point at which the White Nile leaves which lake?

7 Which game is fatal to anyone over 21?

8 To which family of animals does the gnu belong?

9 Which artist painted *The Leaping Horse*?

10 Which museum houses the Elgin Marbles and the Rosetta Stone?

QUIZ 9

RESERVE QUESTIONS
1 How many land miles are there in a league?
2 Which Australian city is served by Tullamarine Airport?
3 Who wrote the score for *A Funny Thing Happened on the Way to the Forum*?

Pub League Quiz 10

The individual questions are in Rounds 5 and 10 and are on the following subjects: Cathedrals, Heraldry, Numbers, Who said? and Soap operas.

Team 1

ROUND 1

1 What is the state capital of Tennessee?
2 Who wrote the play *Major Barbara*?
3 What does KP stand for?
4 What is the name of the leading horse racing course of Paris?
5 Who was the first president of the United Arab Republic?

ROUND 2

1 What name is given to a positive electrode?
2 Motor racing's worst accident was in 1955; over 80 spectators were killed. Where was it?
3 Who starred in the films *Bus Stop* and *The Misfits*?
4 What is the longest river in France?
5 *Eliminator* was in the album charts for over two years. Who recorded it?

Team 2

ROUND 1

1 What is the state capital of Maine?
2 Which dramatist wrote *The Caretaker*?
3 What does MVO stand for?
4 What is the most famous race held at Longchamp?
5 Who became the first chairman of the People's Republic of China?

ROUND 2

1 What name is given to a negative electrode?
2 Who won the Le Mans 24-Hour Race in 1955 and the World Driver's Championship in 1958?
3 What was Marilyn Monroe's real name?
4 In which continent is the Limpopo River?
5 What group did Paul McCartney form after the break-up of the Beatles?

ROUND 3

1 Which TV presenter wrote a book about men?

1 Who played Bella in *Our Mutual Friend,* Mrs Lisa Leeson in *Rogue Trader* and got married to an airman in *Land Girls*?

2 Who founded the world's first Fascist Party?

2 What was Mussolini also known as?

3 What Russian did both Greta Garbo and Vivien Leigh play on screen?

3 Who wrote *Letters from the Underworld*?

4 What is an onager?

4 What is a merino?

5 Before Tony Blair, how many Labour prime ministers had there been?

5 Name three Labour prime ministers before Tony Blair.

ROUND 4

1 In which county is Alton Towers?

1 Which family lives at Hatfield House?

2 From which film is the song 'Moon River'?

2 Who won an Oscar for the song 'Moon River'?

3 What do you get from the product of the length of one side, and its perpendicular distance from the opposite side?

3 Mass times acceleration equals what?

QUIZ
10

4 What is oology the study of?

4 What is etymology?

5 Juneau is the capital of which American state?

5 Which is the 'Keystone State' of the US?

ROUND 5   *Individual questions for team 1*

Cathedrals
In which French cathedral was Charles VII crowned in 1429?

Heraldry
What in heraldry is tincture?

Numbers
Find a number which is less than its square by 72.

Who said?
Who said, 'A week is a long time in politics'?

Soap operas
Which soap did Phil Redmond, formerly of *Grange Hill*, create?

Team 2	Team 1

ROUND 6

Team 2
1. Which famous writer was the son of the curator of the Central Museum at Lahore?
2. Who built the first steam locomotive to run on a railway?
3. Which French province does Camembert cheese come from?
4. What was the name of the minstrel in Robin Hood's gang?
5. In which country is Salamanca?

Team 1
1. Who was born in Bedford, the son of a tinker, and wrote a large part of his most famous book in gaol?
2. In which British city are there railway stations called Foregate Street and Shrub Hill?
3. Of what is marzipan made?
4. How did Robin Hood help the minstrel's bride?
5. In which country is Topeka?

ROUND 7

Team 2
1. To which part of the body does the prefix 'derm' refer?
2. What in heraldry is gold?
3. Who was the winning commander at the naval Battle of the Falklands?
4. What park lies between Buckingham Palace and Piccadilly?
5. What nationality was Pocahontas?

Team 1
1. To which part of the body does the prefix 'cerebro' refer?
2. What in heraldry is silver?
3. Who was the winning commander at Omdurman?
4. Where in Piccadilly is the home of the Royal Academy?
5. What nationality was Count Cavour?

ROUND 8

1 Which playwright wrote *The Master Builder*?
2 What is the name of the small independent state between France and Spain?
3 Give another name for potassium nitrate.
4 Who was the Greek goddess of love?
5 What name is given to a book of words and their synonyms?

1 Which playwright wrote *An Ideal Husband*?
2 What is the southernmost province of Portugal?
3 Which gas is also known as laughing gas?
4 What name did the Romans give to Aphrodite?
5 What name is given to an index of the principal words in a book or in an author's works?

ROUND 9

1 What is the name of the protein present in red blood cells that is scarlet when combined with oxygen?
2 What is the Bengali name for a small rowing boat, used as an auxiliary in yachting?
3 What nationality was the composer Friedrich Smetana?
4 Who was the second man on the moon?
5 What name is given to an abnormally bright star caused by a Crab nebula?

1 What is haemophilia?

2 In what sport are Telemark and Christiana turns used?

3 Which composer wrote a suite entitled *Mother Goose* in English?

QUIZ
10

4 What was the first commercial communications satellite called?
5 Which planet is closest to the sun?

ROUND 10   *Individual questions for team 2*

Cathedrals

In which cathedral was Charlemagne buried?

Heraldry
What in heraldry is a tabard?

Numbers
Divide 48 into two parts so that one is three-fifths of the other.

Who said?
Who said, 'The ballot is stronger than the bullet'?

Soap operas
Which radio Archer died on the opening night of ITV?

Team 1	Team 2

DRINKS ROUND

1 What does IAEA stand for?

1 What does ICAO stand for?

2 Which European country has more than two-fifths of its land below sea level?

2 Name three of the six American states that make up New England.

3 Who wrote *King Solomon's Mines*?

3 Who wrote *The Water Babies*?

4 Who murdered Lee Harvey Oswald?

4 Who murdered Robert Kennedy?

5 Who reigned in England between the years 871 and 899?

5 Who reigned in Scotland between 1040 and 1057?

6 Which actress starred in the film *Boy on a Dolphin*?

6 In which film did Glynis Johns play a mermaid?

7 What is the capital of New Zealand?

7 What is the capital of Luxembourg?

8 What was the name of the Lone Ranger's horse?

8 Whose horse was Trigger in films and TV?

9 In eight hours, Fiona walks three miles more than Jean does in six hours, and in seven hours Jean walks nine miles more than Fiona does in six hours. How many miles does each walk per hour?

10 In which country is Kirkcaldy?

9 Half Edward's age exceeds a quarter of Cyril's by 12 months, and three-quarters of Cyril's age exceeds Edward's by 11 years. How old are they both?

10 In which country is Armagh?

RESERVE QUESTIONS

1 What was President Jimmy Carter's middle name?

2 How many noughts are there in a British billion?

3 Which game is mentioned in Shakespeare's *Antony and Cleopatra*, though it was not invented until the fifteenth century?

Pub League Quiz 11

The individual questions are in Rounds 5 and 10 and are on the following subjects: Films, The arts, Literature, Sport and Proverbs.

Team 1

ROUND 1

1 In which English county would you find both Toronto and Pity Me?

2 Which European country uses the escudo as its unit of currency?

3 In which sport would you hear of a roundhouse, knuckler and outcurve?

4 What is a badger's home called?

5 Which year was India given its independence?

ROUND 2

1 Name the capital of Chile.

2 Who wrote the opera *The Fair Maid of Perth*?

3 What is xenophobia?

4 In Greek mythology, who stole fire from the gods and gave it to mankind?

Team 2

ROUND 1

1 In which English county would you find Wookey Hole?

2 Which country uses the lev as its unit of currency?

3 Kip, crossgrasp and pike are movements in which sport?

4 What is a squirrel's home called?

5 Who was the last Viceroy of India?

ROUND 2

1 Name the capital of Mexico.

2 Who wrote 'A German Requiem' in memory of his mother?

3 Of which disease is hydrophobia a major symptom?

4 By what collective name are Stheno, Euryale and Medusa known?

QUIZ
11

5 Name *Magic Roundabout's* snail.

5 Name *Magic Roundabout's* cow.

ROUND 3

1 Charles Buchinski became a major film star. By what name do we know him?

1 Which American director was famous for his westerns, such a *She Wore a Yellow Ribbon*?

2 Which famous author spent the last 10 years of his life at Gad's Hill?

2 Which fictional French detective always smoked a pipe?

3 What is a dhow?

3 What is a umiak?

4 How long does a game of hockey last?

4 How many active players are there in a water polo team?

5 Which pop group had a 1960s hit with 'When You Walk in the Room'?

5 Who had a 1983 hit with 'Total Eclipse of the Heart'?

ROUND 4

1 Who, in Greek mythology, was the god of marriage?

1 Who in Greek mythology was a surly ferryman?

2 What for William James was 'the bitch goddess'?

2 Who, according to Dorothy Parker, 'ran the whole gamut of emotions from A to B'?

3 Where is Lake Koko-Nor?

3 Where is Lake Como?

4 In what art process would specimens be line-engraved or lithographed?

4 What would a lepidopterist collect?

QUIZ
11

5 What is the common name for the infectious fever variola?

5 Which organ of the body is affected by hepatitis?

ROUND 5 *Individual questions for team 1*

Films
What was the title of the film in which Elvis Presley played a boxer?

The arts
What great French artist is associated with Polynesia?

Literature
Who, famed for his literary works, also invented the pillar box?

Sport
What type of race is run for horses over hunting country?

Proverbs
Complete the proverb, 'Marry in haste and…'

Team 2	Team 1

ROUND 6

1 On whose life did Terence Rattigan base his play *Ross*?

2 Who sang, 'One Day I'll Fly Away'?

3 What is depicted on the reverse of an English two-pence coin?

4 Who wrote *The Secret Seven* series?

5 Who starred in the films *Tom Jones, Charlie Bubbles* and *Annie*?

1 Who wrote the play *Death of a Salesman*?

2 'Touch Me in the Morning' was a hit for which singer?

3 What is on the reverse of an English ten-pence piece?

4 Name Captain Pugwash's boat.

5 Who directed and starred in the silent movies *The Navigator* and *The General*?

QUIZ
11

68

ROUND 7

1 What is a Camberwell Beauty?

2 What is LXX in Roman numerals?

3 What language is spoken in Brazil?

4 How many stars are on the Australian flag?

5 Which football team play at Elland Road?

1 What is a mastiff?

2 In geometry, what do we call a straight line that touches a curve at one point but does not cut it?

3 What is the official language of Cuba?

4 How many stars are on the American flag?

5 Which football team play at Filbert Street?

ROUND 8

1 How many faces has a dodecahedron?

2 Olympic Airways is the national airline of which country?

3 Which French artist was famed for his paintings of prostitutes?

4 What does BDA stand for?

5 What have David Jacobs, Noel Edmonds and Jools Holland all presented on TV?

1 How many sides has a hendecagon?

2 Sabena Airways is the national airline of which country?

3 Which famous artist painted *The Swing*?

4 What does ETD stand for?

5 Who played Quincy in the TV series of the same name?

ROUND 9

1 The General Strike of 1926 was called in support of which union?

2 Which French monarch was known as 'the Sun King'?

1 What other title is held by the First Lord of the Treasury?

2 Charles Beauclerk was the illegitimate son of which English king?

3 Which English city has the postcode LS?

4 Who in the Bible promoted Shadrach, Meshach and Abednego?

5 'Little White Bull' was a hit for which singer?

3 What place is England uses the postcode SS?

4 Name the apostles of Christ whose Christian names begin with the letter 'P'.

5 Which artist sang 'Morning Has Broken'?

ROUND 10   *Individual questions for team 2*

Films
In which film did Mae West say, 'Why don't you come up sometime, see me?'

The arts
Who worked as court painter to Ludovico il Moro of Milan from 1482 to 1499?

Literature
What word describes a break in a line of poetry, often to emphasise an antithesis or comparison?

Sport
Which London soccer club was founded in 1882 by boys from a Presbyterian school?

Proverbs
Complete the proverb, 'The road to hell is paved with…'.

QUIZ 11

Team 1 | *Team 2*

DRINKS ROUND

1 Name the capital of Ethiopia.

2 In which film did Danny Kaye sing 'Wonderful Copenhagen'?

1 Name the chief town of the Shetland Islands.

2 Who wrote and directed *Star Wars*?

3 In which opera is the character Lieutenant Pinkerton?

4 Which metal has the chemical symbol Pb?

5 Which invention began with experiments to aid the deaf?

6 Which country has won most World Curling Championships?

7 What type of creature was Riki Tiki Tavi?

8 Bideford is at the mouth of what river?

9 Which American rock group released 'Riders on the Storm' and 'Light My Fire'?

10 In which sport would the Minnesota Twins play the St Louis Cardinals?

3 Who wrote *The Gondoliers*?

4 Which chemical element has the symbol Cu?

5 Which people reputedly invented paper money?

6 In which sport would you find the following terms: inner, outer and magpie?

7 What type of creatures live in a formicary?

8 On which river does Peterborough stand?

9 Which group had hits with 'Life is a Minestrone' and 'Donna'?

10 Which game is played with white, spot and red balls?

RESERVE QUESTIONS

1 Which planet's satellites are named after characters from Shakespeare?

2 Who is the patron saint of Poland?

3 In which country did the Pied Piper play?

QUIZ 11

Pub League Quiz 12

The individual questions are in Rounds 5 and 10 and are on the following subjects: Pop music, The Olympics, The Bible, What comes next? and Where is it?

Team 1

Team 2

ROUND 1

1 By what name is scorpion grass better known?

1 What flower has the same name as a reddish-orange mineral sometimes used as a gem?

2 Where would you find the Dewey decimal system in use?

2 What are and where would you find the Pleiades?

3 Cousins Manfred B. Lee and Frederic Dannay are better known as whom?

3 Which famous person, in his will, left his wife his furniture and his second-best bed?

4 Where is the *Northern Echo* published?

4 In which town is the *Dorset Evening Echo* published?

5 The town of Moron is in which South American country?

5 The town of Ghent is in which country?

ROUND 2

1 Which pop group sang 'Bits and Pieces'?

1 Which singer was 'Watching the Detectives'?

2 Who wrote, 'When a man is tired of London, he is tired of life; for there is in London all that life can afford'?

2 Who invented the concept of 'doublethink'?

3 Which number in bingo is called half a crown?

3 How many pieces does each side have in draughts?

4 What shipping forecast area lies between Faeroes and Viking?

5 Who opened the first British birth control clinic?

4 What geological era follows the Jurassic?

5 Who founded the East End Mission for destitute children?

ROUND 3

1 Name the year the voting age in Britain became 18?

2 What is the word for a woman's long, double-breasted outer garment, with skirts often cut away in front?

3 Who would use an étrier or a chockstone?

4 In mythology, which gift was given to Cassandra by Apollo?

5 What is the title of the highest ranking judge in the Court of Appeal?

1 In which year did James Dean die?

2 Name the loose over-garment prescribed by law, the distinctive garment of the Jews in the Middle Ages?

3 In which sporting event do the winners only move backwards?

4 Which day of the week is named after a Roman god?

5 How should the Bishop of London be formally addressed?

ROUND 4

1 Which river flows through Lisbon?

2 Name the highest commissioned rank of the Royal Air Force.

3 What ball game is peculiar to Eton College?

1 Moscow stands on which river?

2 The RAF adopted this motto, *Per ardua ad astra*. What does it mean?

3 Which is the first property on a Monopoly board after 'Go'?

QUIZ
12

4 From which area of Spain was Don Quixote supposed to have come?

5 What was Bing Crosby's first baptismal Christian name?

4 In which book would you find the characters Winston Smith and Julia?

5 Which singer sold one million discs of *Who's Sorry Now* and called her autobiography by the same title?

ROUND 5 *Individual questions for team 1*

Pop music
Which folk-rock group had a hit with the album *Angel Delight*?

The Olympics
How many gold medals were won by the USA in the 1980 Summer Olympics?

The Bible
Who in the Bible was asked to interpret the writing on the wall?

What comes next?
2, 17, 3, 19. What comes next?

Where is it?
Where is the Bay of Plenty?

Team 2   *Team 1*

ROUND 6

1 What name is given to the study of the properties and distribution of water?

2 Where is your epiglottis?

3 Who was known as the 'Great Commoner'?

1 What name is given to the art of working metals?

2 What is the epidermis?

3 Who was named 'Supermac' by the cartoonist Vicky in 1958?

QUIZ 12

4 Name the largest of the Greek islands.

5 Of which novel is Fanny Price the heroine?

4 Name the oldest city in Germany on the banks of the Rhine.

5 Who created Frankenstein?

ROUND 7

1 Name the fifth book of the Old Testament.

2 The marrka is the currency of which country?

3 Spider, hermit and masked are all what?

4 What does CBS stand for?

5 What is a double bogey in golf?

1 Which is the only miracle mentioned in all four gospels?

2 What is the unit of currency in Norway?

3 What kind of creature is a copperhead?

4 What does RADA stand for?

5 How many beds has a shove ha'penny board?

ROUND 8

1 How many years is a coral anniversary?

2 Which literary character's favourite expression was, 'Off with his head'?

3 Henry Carey has been credited with the composition and singing of a famous musical work in about 1740. What was it?

4 What was the Christian name of Hardy of Laurel and Hardy fame?

1 What is celebrated on 7 January in the Russian Orthodox Church?

2 Which Thomas Hardy novel ends, 'As soon as they had strength they arose, joined hands again, and went on'?

3 'Strike Up the Band' was written by which American composer and pianist and his brother?

4 What was Stan Laurel's surname at birth?

QUIZ
12

5 Who headed the inquiry into the Brixton riots?

5 Which MP started his political career in 1900 as the successful Tory candidate for Oldham?

ROUND 9

1 Which Shakespeare play begins, 'When shall we three meet again…'?

2 What does a shoat grow up to be?

3 What did Kirkpatrick MacMillan invent in 1839?

4 What is the monetary unit of Singapore?

5 What kind of creature is a barbastelle?

1 Which Shakespeare play begins, 'If music be the food of love …'?

2 What is a female donkey called?

3 Who invented the hot air balloon?

4 What is the monetary unit of Tunisia?

5 What is a pochard?

ROUND 10   *Individual questions for team 2*

Pop music
'Lily the Pink' was a hit for which trio?

The Olympics
Who won four gold medals in the 1936 Berlin Olympics?

The Bible
According to the Bible, who was the father of the Jews?

What comes next?
Who followed Lyndon B. Johnson as president of the USA?

Where is it?
Where is the Hall Napoléon below the Pyramid?

QUIZ 12

Team 1

Team 2

DRINKS ROUND

1 Which British king was styled 'the first gentleman of Europe'?

1 Which British king was described as 'the wisest fool in Christendom'?

2 What type of food is Roquefort?

3 Which football team is nicknamed 'the Canaries'?

4 Which explorer discovered Newfoundland in 1497?

5 What is sodium hydroxide commonly known as?

6 In which countries is Lake Titicaca?

7 Of which country was Juan Peron president?

8 Which 1970s vocal group's singer claimed to be Kaiser Bill's batman?

9 Who was credited with the quotation, 'I never hated a man enough to give him his diamonds back'?

10 In the grounds of which royal residence is St George's Chapel?

2 For which delicacy are the towns of Whitstable and Colchester famous?

3 Which football team is nicknamed 'the Hatters'?

4 What nationality was the explorer Abel Tasman?

5 What is hydrated magnesium sulphate commonly known as?

6 Lake Manitoba is in which country?

7 Who was Israel's first president?

8 'Ride a White Swan' was a hit for which pop group?

9 Who said, 'The House of Lords is the British Outer Mongolia for retired politicians'?

10 On the outside wall of which building can you find Sir Jacob Epstein's bronze statue of St Michael slaying the Devil?

RESERVE QUESTIONS

1 Who composed the rock opera *Tommy*?

2 In which American state is Fort Knox?

3 What name is given to the dish consisting of oysters in bacon?

Pub League Quiz 13

The individual questions are in Rounds 5 and 10 and are on the following subjects: Entertainment, Words, Industry, Finance and Music.

Team 1

ROUND 1
1 Name the capital of Syria.
2 Who wrote the lines, 'Their's not to make reply, their's not to reason why, their's but to do and die'?
3 What does BAFTA stand for?
4 What spirit comes from the terebinth tree?
5 What is the smallest continent?

ROUND 2
1 Which county cricket team play at Trent Bridge?
2 Which part of the body may suffer from opthalmia?
3 Who composed 'Maple Leaf Rag'?

Team 2

1 Name the capital of Turkey.
2 Who wrote the play *Man and Superman*?

3 What does NUJ stand for?
4 What is the name of the solution of shellac in alcohol used by furniture makers?
5 Where in Kent are the Pantiles?

1 Which county cricket team play at Edgbaston?
2 Which part of the body does something 'cutaneous' affect?
3 Who composed the opera *Tales of Hoffmann*?

QUIZ
13

78

4 St Johnstoun once held claim to be the capital of Scotland. By what name is it now known?

5 Which pop singer sang 'Dead Ringer for Love'?

4 Which town in Northern Ireland is the seat of both Protestant and Roman Catholic archbishops?

5 'Twenty-four Hours from Tulsa' was originally a hit for which singer?

ROUND 3

1 Where was the abode of the gods in Greek mythology?

2 Three English kings were killed by arrows. Name two.

1 Name the Greek mountain consecrated to the Muses.

2 Which king quelled the Peasants' Revolt, had Gloucester murdered and was deposed after a rebellion led by Henry Bolingbroke?

3 Which famous actor directed the film *Staying Alive*?

4 Which Englishman painted *Resurrection*, now in the Tate Gallery?

5 In what field did Igor Ivanovich Sikorsky, the Russian inventor, specialise?

3 Which famous actor directed the film *Ordinary People*?

4 *Woman Taken in Adultery* was the work of which Dutch artist?

5 In which field of invention was Sir Frank Whittle a pioneer?

ROUND 4

1 The berry of which tree is used to flavour gin?

2 What is a topgallant?

3 What is mixed with nickel to make nickel silver?

1 What spirit forms the main ingredient of Daiquiri?

2 What is a bain-marie?

3 Which metal is derived from the mineral cinnabar?

QUIZ 13

79

4 Who sang 'North to Alaska' on record?

5 In which war was Britain engaged between 1899 and 1902?

4 Who wrote the novel *Northwest Passage*?

5 The Germans call a First World War sea battle the Battle of the Skagerrak. What do the British call it?

ROUND 5   *Individual questions for team 1*

Entertainment
Who founded the 'Method' school of acting?

Words
If you suffered from pyrophobia what would you fear?

Industry
What is processed in a ginnery?

Finance
What is the US equivalent of the FTSE Index?

Music
Name the bandleader who died in an air crash over the English Channel during the Second World War.

Team 2   *Team 1*

ROUND 6

1 In which London street is the Garrick Club?

1 What post for travellers is kept for a limited period at a specified post office?

2 What is the name of the Vatican's army?

2 Which religious body was founded by George Fox?

3 Which sport do you associate with the Los Angeles Lakers?

3 Which sport would you associate with the Boston Red Sox?

4 Which famous building would you find at Agra?

4 Where in London is the Whispering Gallery?

5 In which field of art was Barbara Hepworth famous?

5 In which of the arts did Joan Sutherland achieve fame?

ROUND 7

1 Who discovered Brazil?

1 Who first explored the River Amazon?

2 Which planet shares its name with a glass sponge called a flower-basket?

2 Which planet was discovered in 1846?

3 What was the Manhattan Project?

3 Why was the poppy chosen for Remembrance Sunday?

4 The name of which branch of mathematics means triangle measurement?

4 If a clock seen in a mirror is read as 2.40 what time is it?

5 Which pop group sang 'He Ain't Heavy, He's My Brother'?

5 Which soul singer was 'Sittin' on the Dock of the Bay'?

ROUND 8

1 In which country are the ruins of Carthage?

1 Who was responsible for the Domesday Book?

2 In which English county is Hartland Point?

2 Which new town in Shropshire was named after a local engineer?

3 What was the maiden name of Jacqueline Kennedy-Onassis?

3 Who was known as 'Madame Deficit'?

4 What perennial East Indian plant is used in curry powder and also as a chemical indicator of alkalis?

4 What is another name for endive?

5 Name the science of correcting deformities of bones, joints, ligaments, muscles and tendons.

5 What name is given to the kind of mistakes in speech, in which a person mixes up the initial sounds of words.

QUIZ
13

ROUND 9

1 If you were born on 1 October what would your astrological sun sign be?

1 What sun sign covers birthdays from 21 March to 20 April?

2 Which Egyptian leader was assassinated in 1981?

2 Which statesman was assassinated on 15 March 44 BC?

3 In which TV soap did Cliff Barnes appear?

3 Who played Sable Colby in *Dynasty*?

4 What is the popular name for Tchaikovsky's Symphony No. 6 in B Minor?

4 What is the popular name for Beethoven's Symphony No. 9 in D Minor?

5 What English word from the Greek for black means sadness?

5 What English word from the Greek for black describes the pigment that makes human hair and skin dark?

ROUND 10   *Individual questions for team 2*

Entertainment
Which city burned in *Gone With the Wind*?

Words
'*Veni, vidi, vici*' were famous words of Julius Caesar. What do they mean?

Industry
What is dried in oast houses?

Finance
What is GNP?

Music
Which American composed the ballet music for *On the Town*?

Team 1	*Team 2*

DRINKS ROUND

1 Which phrase devised by Joseph Heller means a no-win situation?

1 What does the phrase *exempli gratia* mean in English?

2 What is a sphygmomanometer used for?

2 What is tinnitus?

3 Balm, dill and sorrel are all what?

3 Foreman, Longman, Lechman, Little Man and Thuma are always found together. Why?

4 What sort of musical instrument was a timbal?

4 Long before it became a popular operatic piece, a barcarole used to be sung by whom?

5 This Dutchman died in 1939. During the First World War he designed German aircraft. Who was he?

5 Which German developed the V2 and later the Saturn rockets?

6 What is the name of the chief muscle used in breathing?

6 What is the other name for the scapula?

7 Which painter is credited with the development of pointillism?

7 Which painter was shot by the actress Valeria Solarnis?

8 Who succeeded Hoover as president of the USA?

8 Which American president followed James Buchanan?

9 Name the stretch of water that separates the Inner and Outer Hebrides.

9 Puffin Island gets its name from the birds that breed there. Where is Puffin Island?

10 Who was prime minister of Great Britain from 1955–57?

10 Who became prime minister of Israel in 1969?

RESERVE QUESTIONS
1 What did John Logie Baird invent?
2 What name is given to the sea route from the Atlantic round the north of Canada to the Pacific?
3 Name the Greek goddess of peace.

QUIZ
13

Pub League Quiz 14

The individual questions are in Rounds 5 and 10 and are on the following subjects: The Bible, Opera, Mythology, Trees and plants, and Games and pastimes.

Team 1

Team 2

ROUND 1

1 Which English king was beheaded in 1649?
2 What is the correct title of the painting known as *The Rokeby Venus*?
3 Within five, how many symphonies did Haydn write?
4 During which king's reign was the 'Bloody Assize' held?
5 Which card is removed from the pack at the beginning of the game Pope Joan?

1 What caused Prince Albert's death in 1861?
2 Which famous picture did Basil Hallward paint?
3 Within five, what is the atomic number for plutonium?
4 What were Charles I's supporters called in the Civil War?
5 Bamboos are one of three suits in which game?

ROUND 2

1 'From the earth thou springest, Like a cloud of fire'. To what was Shelley referring?
2 Name the largest of the Society Islands which was visited by Captain Cook and William Bligh.
3 In Greek mythology, by what was the sword of Damocles suspended?

1 Which twentieth-century English poet wrote about Rannoch by Glencoe?
2 In which Irish county are Ballymena and Ballymoney?
3 Who, in Greek mythology, was the equivalent of the Roman god Saturn?

4 What is Eva Herzigova famous for modelling?

5 Who composed the opera *Boris Godunov*?

ROUND 3

1 Who wrote *A Farewell to Arms*?

2 Where is the San Andreas Fault?

3 Umbles can be made into a pie and gave rise to the expression to eat (H)umble pie. What are umbles?

4 Who succeeded Alf Ramsey as England's soccer manager?

5 What does ICBM stand for?

ROUND 4

1 What is the capital of Sierra Leone?

2 What kind of plane was an Avro Lancaster?

3 Who was David Copperfield's nurse?

4 Which town did Slade come from?

5 What is the name of the House of Representatives of the national parliament of the Republic of Ireland?

4 Who was the first *haute couture* designer to show a collection for men?

5 Who composed the opera *Duke Bluebeard's Castle*?

1 Who wrote *The Mallen* trilogy of novels?

2 On which island is Adams Peak?

3 *Gnocchi* is a food from Italy. What is it?

4 Who was the first footballer to be knighted?

5 What does SALT stand for?

1 What is the capital of Jamaica?

2 Which country developed Mirage warplanes?

3 Who wrote the original bestseller about Provence?

4 Where did the Rolling Stones give a free concert in 1969, when 3000 butterflies were released in memory of Brian Jones?

5 Which statesman who died in 1527 gave his name to a word meaning unscrupulous political cunning?

QUIZ
14

85

ROUND 5   *Individual questions for team 1*

The Bible
In the New Testament, which book follows the four gospels?

Opera
In which of Mozart's operas does the statue of the murdered Commandant come to life?

Mythology
Who was the ancient Egyptian god of the sun?

Trees and plants
'Scotch' and 'wych' are two species of which tree?

Games and pastimes
A game played with a small hour-glass-shaped object spun on a string fastened to two sticks was once know as 'Devil on Two Sticks'. By what name is it now familiarly known?

Team 2	Team 1

ROUND 6

1. How many chambers has the human heart?

2. On a three-masted vessel, which mast is the mizzen mast?

3. What was the official residence of the British sovereign between 1689 and 1837?

4. Which British doctor became famous for his concept of lateral thinking?

5. In which country is Lusaka?

1. What is the part of the small intestine leading from the stomach in humans called?

2. How many masts has a yawl?

3. A tollbooth was used as a customs house or a town house. To what other use was it sometimes put?

4. Whose accurate observation of the moon helped Newton to formulate the laws of gravity?

5. Badwater is the western hemisphere's lowest point. Where is it?

ROUND 7

1 *Henrietta Temple* was a novel by which statesman?
2 In which county are Mousehole and Indian Queens?
3 With which of the arts was Sergei Diaghilev associated?
4 In which year did George V become king?
5 From what is the liqueur calvados made?

1 By what name is writer David John Moore Cornwell better known?
2 Queensferry is a royal burgh of which city?
3 Who designed the tapestry for the rebuilt Coventry Cathedral?
4 Who was king of England after Richard I?
5 With what is Grand Marnier flavoured?

ROUND 8

1 How many grains go into a scruple?
2 What is a Suffolk Punch?
3 How many volleyball players are there on each side?
4 Who was the original presenter of television's *Question Time*?
5 What is the offspring of a male ass and a mare?

1 How many psalms are in the Book of Psalms?
2 What is lexicography?
3 Who won the men's singles at Wimbledon in 1993, 1994 and 1998?
4 Who hosted the TV show *Call My Bluff*?
5 What dog of African origin cannot bark?

ROUND 9

1 Which queen's divorce is one of the principal incidents of Shakespeare's *Henry VIII*?
2 Name the disease of the eye in which the lens becomes opaque.

1 In *Hamlet*, whose grave was being dug when Yorick's skull was unearthed?
2 Where is the jugular vein?

3 What Hindi word means both 'curtain' and 'seclusion of women'?

4 Who wrote *A Tale of a Tub* in 1704?

5 In which year was the Aberfan disaster?

3 What is the Hindi word for 'holy war'?

4 Who wrote *Rich Man, Poor Man*?

5 Who in 1985 became the youngest world chess champion ever?

ROUND 10   *Individual questions for team 2*

The Bible
Who was the wife of both Uriah the Hittite and David?

Opera
Which Gilbert and Sullivan opera is subtitled *A Merryman and His Maid*?

Mythology
Who was the nymph who was changed into a laurel bush to save her from Apollo?

Trees and plants
Give another name for the underground stem of a potato.

Games and pastimes
Which playing card is sometimes referred to as the 'Black Lady'?

Team 1

Team 2

DRINKS ROUND

1 Which post-war prime minister represented the constituencies of Stockton-on-Tees (1924–9 and 1931–45) and Bromley (1945–64)?

1 Which prime minister lived at Hughenden House, north of High Wycombe?

2 Dorothea Brooke is the heroine in which George Eliot book?

3 Who packed her trunk and said goodbye to the circus?

4 Abu Simbel is in which river valley?

5 What would the garnish be if something was *à la Crécy*?

6 What is a davenport?

7 On whose book was the film *Strangers on a Train* based?

8 What comedian sang about 'Careless Hands' in 1967 and 'Loneliness' in 1969?

9 What novel by M.M. Kaye ends, 'And it may even be that they found their Kingdom'?

10 What is the meaning of the abbreviation ASH?

2 Who wrote *Erewhon*?

3 What was the name of Andy Pandy's girlfriend?

4 In which country is Agadir?

5 If something is *dubarry*, what will one of the ingredients be?

6 What is a matrass?

7 On whose play was the film *Witness for the Prosecution* based?

8 Who sang 'Tie Me Kangaroo Down, Sport'?

9 What book begins, 'The Mole had been working very hard all morning'?

10 What does ESP stand for?

RESERVE QUESTIONS

1 In which Dickens novel do Thomas Gradgrind and Josiah Bounderby appear?

2 What drug is named after an ancient god of dreams?

3 How many office-holding cardinals are permanently resident in England?

QUIZ
14

The Answers

Pub League Quiz 1 Answers

Team 1	*Team 2*

ROUND 1

	Team 1		Team 2
1	Thor Heyerdahl.	1	To prove that reed boats could have crossed the Atlantic Ocean.
2	Edouard Lalo.	2	Georges Bizet.
3	Europe.	3	Africa.
4	Sir Walter Scott.	4	Alfred, Lord Tennyson.
5	James II and his Stuart descendants.	5	Charles I.

ROUND 2

	Team 1		Team 2
1	A crab.	1	Capricorn.
2	'Puppet on a String'.	2	H.E. Bates.
3	The eland.	3	An eel-like fish.
4	Inveraray.	4	County Durham.
5	Hanover.	5	Mary, Queen of Scots.

ROUND 3

	Team 1		Team 2
1	Radio detection and ranging.	1	Organisation de l'Armée Secrète or Organisation of American States.
2	Mars.	2	Venus.
3	Wallace Hume Carothers.	3	John Deere.
4	By right or by lawful right.	4	1949.
5	Freddie Mercury.	5	*Dangerous*.

ROUND 4

	Team 1		Team 2
1	Mrs Sirimavo Bandaranaike.	1	Charlotte Corday.
2	The collar bone.	2	Over your shoulder joint.
3	Pat Eddery.	3	John Naber.
4	Ottawa.	4	Adelaide.
5	Nicholas Monsarrat.	5	Sir Thomas More.

ROUND 5

Films
The Taming of the Shrew
(Shakespeare).

Sport
Ty Cobb.

Science
The speed of light.

Pot luck
Tenor.

Geography
Arctic plains or deserts.

Team 2

Team 1

ROUND 6
1   Chlorophyll.
2   A trout.
3   Norman Mailer.
4   Fine Gael.
5   St Nicholas.

1   Wolfram.
2   A jack.
3   John le Carré.
4   1911.
5   St Denis.

ROUND 7
1   Granddaughter.
2   Brian Jones.
3   4,840.
4   Benjamin Franklin.
5   Peter Sellers.

1   Great-grandson.
2   Franz Schubert.
3   640.
4   Edmund Cartwright.
5   Harry Secombe.

ROUND 8
1   Arnold Bennett's.
2   A diving bird.
3   W.A. Mozart.
4   Olive Oyl.
5   Five.

1   Thomas Hardy's.
2   A fish.
3   Four.
4   Dennis the Menace.
5   The *Trimurti*.

ROUND 9
1   Adolphe Adam.
2   Golgotha or Calvary.
3   W.C. Fields.

4   Richard Oastler.

1   The Hebrides Overture.
2   Gethsemane.
3   William Claude
    Dukenfeld.
4   Wat Tyler.

5   Stentor.

5   Sir Galahad.

ROUND 10

Films
James Cagney *(Yankee Doodle Dandy)*.

Sport
Maureen Connolly.

Science
Homeopathy.

Pot luck
Gilbert White.

Geography
Sargasso Sea.

Team 1

Team 2

DRINKS ROUND

1   Geoffrey Chaucer.
2   Royal Army Pay Corps.
3   Manila.
4   A peach.
5   Michelangelo.
6   1948.
7   Aretha Franklin.
8   Six.

9   Random Access Memory.
10 Larkspur.

1   Herman Melville.
2   Royal Logistic Corps.
3   Caracas.
4   Orange.
5   Caravaggio.
6   George Eastman.
7   Fleetwood Mac.
8   France, West Germany, the Netherlands, Belgium, Luxembourg and Italy.
9   Read Only Memory.
10 The tobacco plant.

RESERVE QUESTIONS
1   Hercule Poirot.
2   Alcatraz.
3   Archie Hahn.

Pub League Quiz 2 Answers

Team 1

Team 2

ROUND 1
1   Purple or red.
2   The cinema organ.
3   The franc.
4   Green, white and red.
5   Sea of Marmora.

1   Green.
2   The trumpet.
3   The quetzal.
4   Red, white and black.
5   Italy.

ROUND 2
1   The Magna Carta was signed.
2   A musical instrument.

3   Wind speed or force.

4   One (*The Red Vineyard*, sold to Belgian artist Anna Boch).
5   Ernest Hemingway.

1   St Helena.

2   A corruption of Bethlehem. The Bethlehem Hospital, Bishopsgate, London, was converted into a lunatic asylum.
3   An instrument used to measure the velocity of a fluid flow.
4   René Magritte.

5   Jane Austen.

ROUND 3
1   Marvin Gaye.
2   They drew after extra time and had to have a replay.
3   *Middlemarch*.
4   Bangladesh.
5   Harold Macmillan.

1   Cliff Richard.
2   Ingemar Johansson.

3   *A Clockwork Orange*.
4   The Dolomites.
5   Winston S. Churchill.

ROUND 4
1   The Duke of Medina Sidonia.

1   Lord Howard of Effingham.

2   British Airways.
3   Longships.
4   Man Ray.
5   1945.

2   Martini.
3   Eddystone.
4   Daniel Mytens.
5   Stalingrad.

ROUND 5

Films
Olivia de Havilland.

The arts
The Rite of Spring by Igor
Stravinsky.

Paris
Pont Neuf.

Who said?
David Lloyd George.

World leaders
Fitzgerald.

Team 2

Team 1

ROUND 6
1   Legendary giants.
2   Slowly with broad dignity.
3   Victoria Tower.
4   The Bible.
5   Australia.

1   Beowulf.
2   *Sostenuto.*
3   Cheltenham.
4   Three.
5   Italy.

ROUND 7
1   Denmark.
2   John Milton.

3   Canada.
4   *Zwanzig.*
5   Kenya.

1   Iceland.
2   'The Burial of Sir John
    Moore After Corunna'
    (Charles Wolfe).
3   Utah.
4   *Otto.*
5   USA.

ROUND 8
1   The right to take from
    wood or wasteland a
    reasonable portion of
    wood for use in the home.

2   Ozone.
3   Diana Rigg.

1   A right of way over land
    for access only, as in the
    case of the carriage of
    minerals from a mine or
    quarry.
2   The element chromium.
3   Honor Blackman.

4 A garden summer-house.
5 Royal College of
Veterinary Surgeons.

ROUND 9
1 Tuberculosis.
2 Himself.
3 Greyhounds.

4 The Friendly Islands.
5 Magpie.

ROUND 10
Films
Raymond Massey.

The arts
Horse racing, ballet and
women washing.

Team 1

DRINKS ROUND
1 Honey and plenty of
money wrapped up in a
five pound note.
2 *Hamlet.*
3 God willing.
4 The Louvre, Paris.
5 Ramadan.
6 Argentina.
7 General Noriega of
Panama.
8 A shoulder cape with
elongated sides.
9 Saxophone.
10 Peter Sallis.

RESERVE QUESTIONS
1 James Cook.
2 The epicentre.
3 Stanley Baldwin.

4 Campanile.
5 European Free Trade
Association.

1 In a motorcycle accident.
2 Alexander the Great.
3 The Derby is for three-
year-olds only.
4 Vancouver Island.
5 A sunken fence, hedge
or wall.

Paris
Montmartre.

Who said?
Winston S. Churchill.

World leaders
Archbishop Makarios.

Team 2

1 On Wednesday he was
married.

2 Uriah Heep.
3 Of sound mind.
4 Antwerp.
5 Armageddon.
6 Greece (Macedonia).
7 Olaf Palme.

8 A close-fitting cap.

9 Charlie Parker.
10 Raymond Burr.

Pub League Quiz 3 Answers

Team 1

ANSWERS
(QUIZ 3)

ROUND 1
1 Irving Berlin.

2 C.
3 Kings of Siam used to give an elephant to people they disliked since the cost of keeping one was more trouble than it was worth.
4 Before the reign of Richard I.
5 Clement Attlee.

ROUND 2
1 An Australian snake.
2 Fellow of the Royal Geographical Society.
3 Oxford
4 J.M.W. Turner.
5 518 feet.

ROUND 3
1 The Netherlands.
2 1984.
3 Caves.
4 Finland.
5 Tristan da Cunha.

ROUND 4
1 Uruguay.
2 William II.
3 Sergei Prokofiev.
4 Indian Ocean.
5 Culture Beat.

Team 2

ROUND 1
1 Bob Geldof and Midge Ure.
2 Q.
3 Down a mine. It is the miners' name for methane.

4 A year and a day.

5 Hugh Gaitskell.

ROUND 2
1 A griffon.
2 National Union of Students.
3 Bristol.
4 Sir Alfred Gilbert.
5 984 feet.

ROUND 3
1 Toledo.
2 Rowing or sculling.
3 A deputy or substitute.
4 Poland.
5 Willem Barents and Jacob Heemskerk.

ROUND 4
1 Uruguay.
2 The Court of Verderers.
3 British.
4 Mahé.
5 Vince Clarke.

ROUND 5

Pot luck
A plug at the mouth of some wind instruments.

History
Captain (later Sir) Henry Morgan.

Politics
William Wilberforce.

Biology
Eighty beats a minute.

Art
Michelangelo.

Team 2

Team 1

ROUND 6
1 Amen.

2 16.
3 Arabic, English, French.
4 San Francisco.
5 Detroit.

1 Genesis, Exodus and Leviticus.
2 18.
3 Christian, Muslim, Druse.
4 A brand new jersey.
5 Red.

ROUND 7
1 The storm (or stormy) petrel.
2 Eight.

3 Edward I.
4 Prague.
5 Ice hockey.

1 The missel thrush.
2 Noun, pronoun, adjective, adverb, verb, preposition, conjunction, interjection.
3 Edward I.
4 Delhi.
5 Rowing.

ROUND 8
1 Kublai Khan.

2 La Manche.
3 William Arthur Philip Louis.
4 David Janssen.
5 Chromium.

1 'The Ballad of Reading Gaol' (Oscar Wilde).
2 The bends.
3 Kenya.

4 A one-armed man.
5 Chromite.

ROUND 9
1 La Paz.
2 Georgy Porgy.

1 Port of Spain.
2 The Great Plague 1665–6.

3   Mexico.
4   The afghani.
5   1983.

3   Staffa, Inner Hebrides.
4   The krona.
5   Moorgate.

ROUND 10

Pot luck
Calcutta.

Biology
Eugenics.

History
Alfred Dreyfus.

Art
Raphael.

Politics
Josip Broz.

Team 1

Team 2

DRINKS ROUND
1   Pampas.
2   Wilkie Collins.
3   Helena.
4   Three.
5   'Enola Gay'.

1   The Mistral.
2   Nancy Mitford.
3   Mont Blanc.
4   Sulphuric acid.
5   *The Duke of Gloucester* (1954).

6   Sweden.
7   Mace.
8   France.
9   Goliath.
10   Four points.

6   Germany.
7   Seaweed.
8   Sudan.
9   Reggae.
10   Two points.

RESERVE QUESTIONS
1   Norway, Sweden, Finland and Russia.
2   Sarajevo.
3   Globe, Jerusalem and Chinese.

Pub League Quiz 4 Answers

Team 1

Team 2

ROUND 1
1   Clint Eastwood.

1   Warren Beatty.

2   J. Fenimore Cooper.
3   Esperanto.
4   The TT Races.
5   The Italian Republic.

2   Iago.
3   1887.
4   Tourist Trophy.
5   The Quai d'Orsay.

ROUND 2
1   Ariel.
2   Apollo 11.
3   The hip.
4   Fellow of the Institute of Actuaries.
5   Detective/police thriller.

1   Gertrude.
2   Laika.
3   Clematis.
4   Fellow of the Chartered Institute of Bankers.
5   Van der Valk.

ROUND 3
1   A stew of lamb with root vegetables.

1   A dessert made from cream beaten with sugar, wine or cider and often lemon juice.

2   Protestant.
3   Benjamin Disraeli.
4   Tony Jacklin.
5   Joseph.

2   Roman Catholic.
3   *Vivian Grey*.
4   Tiger country.
5   Joshua.

ROUND 4
1   David Bowie.
2   Israel.
3   Five.
4   Merlin.
5   Gazetteer.

1   In white satin.
2   Romania.
3   Ten pence.
4   Camelot.
5   Mycology.

ROUND 5

Kings and queens
King Louis XVI of France.

Places
Porcelain.

Famous men
John F. Kennedy.

General knowledge
They were built as defences against invasion during the Napoleonic Wars.

Sport
White.

Team 2

Team 1

ROUND 6
1   Mercury and Venus.

1   Mercury and Venus.

99

2   Sarah Catherine Martin.
3   The Storting.
4   Vincente Minnelli.

5   Victor Hugo.

2   Oliver Postgate.
3   The University of Paris.
4   Tim Rice and Andrew Lloyd Webber.
5   Boris Pasternak.

ROUND 7
1   Mexico.
2   Gopher wood.
3   Mounted guns, cannons and artillery.
4   John Gay.
5   Peru.

1   Rio Grande.
2   The Dead Sea Scrolls.
3   Turkey and Egypt.

4   The Old Testament.
5   The Scarlet Pimpernel.

ROUND 8
1   Thomas Gray.
2   Cleopatra's Needle.
3   Jon Pertwee.
4   South Africa.
5   Road making: macadamising, from which tarmac developed.

1   Percy Bysshe Shelley.
2   1440.
3   Una Stubbs.
4   Greece.
5   The Mini Minor.

ROUND 9
1   Its footprint.

2   Napoleon I (Bonaparte).
3   The strings.
4   Joseph.
5   Eire (1938—45).

1   The offence of trading in church offices.
2   Voltaire.
3   A flute.
4   Mary Magdalene.
5   Spanish.

ROUND 10

Kings and queens
William the Conqueror (William I).

Famous men
He died of a self-inflicted gunshot wound.

Sport
1912.

Places
Uxbridge.

General knowledge
Anthony Wedgwood (Tony) Benn.

Team 1	Team 2

DRINKS ROUND

	Team 1		Team 2
1	St Mark.	1	St James ('the Greater').
2	Thomas à Becket.	2	Leon Trotsky.
3	Major-General.	3	Commodore.
4	The sol.	4	The rupee.
5	Stendhal.	5	Honoré de Balzac.
6	Boris Karloff.	6	Tony Curtis.
7	Burma.	7	England.
8	Five.	8	Four.
9	Canada.	9	Wales.
10	Trevor Eve.	10	Jeremy Irons.

ANSWERS (QUIZ 5)

RESERVE QUESTIONS
1 A dinner jacket.
2 Butter.
3 Drink from it.

Pub League Quiz 5 Answers

Team 1	Team 2

ROUND 1

	Team 1		Team 2
1	A bird.	1	The coyote.
2	Bobby Moore.	2	Gerd Müller.
3	Montreal.	3	Hereford United.
4	Munster.	4	Clare, Cork, Kerry, Limerick, Tipperary and Waterford.
5	Boris Pasternak.	5	Captain Frederick Marryat.

ROUND 2

	Team 1		Team 2
1	Felix Mendelssohn.	1	Seven.
2	William Bateson.	2	St Mary's.
3	Fellow of the Royal College of Surgeons.	3	Fellow of the Royal Horticultural Society.
4	Peter Lorre.	4	Hungary.
5	River Danube.	5	Switzerland.

ROUND 3

1 A little over 40 mph (41.98 mph).
2 Gladys Knight and the Pips.
3 Eric Morecambe.
4 A 'fairy'.
5 The Yorkshire Ripper.

1 A little over nine minutes.
2 The Kinks.
3 Ernie.
4 Africa.
5 Idi Amin.

ROUND 4

1 The cuttlefish.
2 Giacomo Matteoti's.
3 Custard pies.
4 Claudius I.
5 John Cleese.

1 10.
2 Prime Minister of South Africa.
3 Speedy Gonzales.
4 Richard II.
5 Prunella Scales.

ROUND 5

Mythology and legend
Athena's.

Africa
Togo.

Entertainment
Moulin Rouge.

People and places
Crete (named after King Minos).

Numbers
A £12, B £20, C £34.

Team 2
___

Team 1
___

ROUND 6

1 Dr Elizabeth Garrett Anderson, 1908.
2 Sir Malcolm Sargent.
3 The Albert Medal.
4 William Somerset Maugham.
5 Leo.

1 St Augustine.
2 She led the women's suffrage movement.
3 The Congressional Medal of Honor.
4 William Shakespeare.
5 Sagittarius.

ROUND 7

1 Benjamin Disraeli.

1 Napoleon Bonaparte.

102

2	John XIII.	2	John Paul I.
3	The Mountains of Mourne.	3	Slieve Donard.
4	*Faith.*	4	Paul Simon.
5	An instrument for measuring specific gravity.	5	An instrument that measures magnetic forces, especially of the earth.

ROUND 8

1	Iceland (The Althing, AD 930).	1	German.
2	Venus.	2	Venus.
3	John Creasey.	3	G.K. Chesterton.
4	Ava Gardner.	4	Joan Crawford.
5	10.	5	The triple jump.

ROUND 9

1	Hampshire.	1	Gloucestershire.
2	Polo.	2	Show jumping.
3	Solomon.	3	'Thou shalt have no other gods before me'.
4	Cole Porter.	4	Vaudeville.
5	Richard Dimbleby.	5	The Light, Home and Third Programmes.

ROUND 10

Mythology and legend
Cupid.

People and places
Public opinion polls.

Africa
Mali.

Numbers
Seven, nine.

Entertainment
Lou Ferrigno.

Team 1	*Team 2*

DRINKS ROUND

1	Entrecôte.	1	Cod's roe (sometimes grey mullet's).
2	The soldier of Rupert Brooke.	2	Empty tomb.
3	Water.	3	Nitrogen.
4	Robert Donat.	4	Ingrid Bergman.
5	Bright green.	5	Yellow.

6	Three days and nights.	6	Salome.
7	Tennessee Williams.	7	Emlyn Williams.
8	Osbert Lancaster.	8	William Heath Robinson.
9	1660.	9	1867.
10	Linus.	10	Minnie.

RESERVE QUESTIONS
1 A song bird.
2 Russia.
3 Albany.

Pub League Quiz 6 Answers

Team 1   **Team 2**

ROUND 1

Team 1		Team 2	
1	A shallow ornamental bowl or cup mounted on a base.	1	A large stone used in prehistoric constructions (e.g. Stonehenge).
2	Thomas Edison.	2	Georges Clemenceau.
3	All of them.	3	*Falstaff.*
4	Nell Dunn.	4	Paul Scott.
5	Tony Blair.	5	Baroness Thatcher of Kesteven.

ROUND 2

Team 1		Team 2	
1	Quinine.	1	Anaesthetic.
2	Siam.	2	Oxonian.
3	Yom Kippur.	3	The religious coming of age of a 13-year-old Jewish boy.
4	Stanley Baldwin.	4	Harry S. Truman.
5	An instrument for producing and photographing a spectrum.	5	An instrument for signalling using the sun or for photographing the sun.

ROUND 3

Team 1		Team 2	
1	The Urals.	1	The Yellow River.
2	Queen's Park.	2	22 yards.

3   Kaaba.
4   Navy, Army and Air Force Institutes.
5   Richard Harris.

3   Hinduism.
4   International Standard Book Number.
5   Margaret Lockwood.

ROUND 4
1   Edward VI.
2   Swastika.
3   Robert Burns.
4   Richard Ingrams.
5   Metro-Goldwyn-Mayer.

1   95.
2   Fascism.
3   Ella Wheeler Wilcox.
4   John Lennon.
5   RKO.

ROUND 5

Classical music
Hector Berlioz.

Motoring
1905.

History
John Bellingham.

Television
Callan.

Chance
India and Sri Lanka.

ANSWERS (QUIZ 6)

Team 2

Team 1

ROUND 6
1   Australia.
2   Margaret Mitchell.
3   Allah.
4   Fellow of the Royal Society of Literature.
5   Armagnac.

1   California.
2   Evelyn Waugh.
3   The head of John the Baptist.
4   Naval Officer in Charge.
5   A very dry sherry.

ROUND 7
1   Greece.
2   Karate.
3   Clouds.
4   John Keats.
5   Sir Alec Douglas-Home.

1   Horatio Nelson.
2   Jujitsu (or Judo).
3   Dystopia.
4   William Wordsworth.
5   P.I. Tchaikovsky.

ROUND 8

1 Mr Pastry.

1 *Help, A Hard Day's Night, Yellow Submarine, Magical Mystery Tour, Let It Be.*

2 Trinity House.
3 Ski-ing.

2 Portsmouth.
3 New South Wales, Australia.

4 *Kitsch*.
5 Sir Henry Morton Stanley and Dr David Livingstone.

4 Grandma Moses.
5 Sherlock Holmes and Professor Moriarty.

ROUND 9

1 Node.
2 Rock Hudson.
3 Cervix.
4 District of Columbia.

1 Taproot.
2 Nigel Havers.
3 The common cold.
4 Airborne Warning and Control System.

5 Charlie Peace.

5 A black hat.

ROUND 10

Classical music
Franz Joseph Haydn.

Television
What the Papers Say.

Motoring
He invented catseyes.

Chance
Master of Surgery.

History
Anne Boleyn.

Team 1

Team 2

DRINKS ROUND

1 Map making.
2 False.
3 Castor and Pollux.

1 Tonga.
2 True.
3 Procustes was a monster who killed his victims by stretching them, or cutting off their legs, to fit into his bed.

4 The outer.
5 Baseball.

4 The bar.
5 Soccer; it is the World Cup.

6 The Special Theory of Relativity.

6 Albert Einstein.

7 Victor Hugo.

7 John Masters.

8 A light coloured horse (or a pigeon or dove).

8 A small South American bird.

9 Garbage In, Garbage Out.

9 Antimony.

10 Skye.

10 Loch Lomond.

RESERVE QUESTIONS
1 David Low.
2 Chicago.
3 Madonna.

Pub League Quiz 7 Answers

Team 1

Team 2

ROUND 1
1 George Pompidou.

1 Andrew Bonar Law.

2 G.K. Chesterton.

2 Richard Brinsley Sheridan.

3 A second.

3 Sulphur.

4 Thomas Arne.

4 George Frederick Handel.

5 Four.

5 High jump.

ROUND 2
1 Kappa.

1 Delta.

2 Auguste Rodin.

2 Miniatures.

3 The Lavender Hill Mob.

3 Rod Steiger.

4 Spain.

4 The Ottawa River.

5 Gibraltar.

5 Colonel Thomas Blood.

ROUND 3
1 World Council of Churches.

1 Confederation of British Industry.

2 Graham Greene.

2 Ernest Hemingway.

3 Malaysia.

3 Morgan.

4 Calculus.

4 From the Latin, *salarium*, meaning salt, with which Roman soldiers were paid.

5 Cole Porter.

5 Jerome Kern.

107

ROUND 4

1	A duck.	1	A lizard.
2	The period directly before Christmas.	2	The coming.
3	William Kent.	3	John Nash.
4	*Citizen Kane.*	4	A New York subway train.
5	South Atlantic Ocean.	5	Indian Ocean.

ROUND 5

Holiday and travel
The Isle of Man.

The Bible
Zacharias and Elizabeth.

Food and drink
Tortilla.

History
Son-in-law.

Music
Johann Sebastian Bach.

Team 2   *Team 1*

ROUND 6

1	Limestone and clay.	1	Bauxite.
2	The pancreas.	2	The ear.
3	The London Marathon.	3	Wigan.
4	The Sugdens.	4	'Dirty Den' Watts.
5	Mitre.	5	Sarong.

ROUND 7

1	A Spanish princess.	1	A Polish dance.
2	Islamabad.	2	Halifax.
3	D. H. Lawrence.	3	David Herbert.
4	Royal Naval Volunteer Reserve.	4	Royal Canadian Mounted Police.
5	Denis Healey.	5	Edward Heath.

ROUND 8

1	A citrus.	1	Sequoia or redwood.
2	The Battle of Trafalgar.	2	The Battle of Culloden.
3	Jersey Joe Walcott.	3	Bob Fitzsimmons.
4	The shins.	4	A crusade.

| 5 | The River Itchen. | 5 | The Ouse and Trent. |

ROUND 9

1	Switzerland.	1	D.
2	Edward I.	2	The Battle of the Boyne.
3	They are names of stud poker games.	3	78.
4	Ted Hughes.	4	John Masefield.
5	Mexico.	5	Argentina and Chile.

ROUND 10

Holiday and travel
Her Britannic Majesty's
Secretary of State.

Food and drink
Potatoes.

Music
Ludwig van Beethoven.

The Bible
The temple at Jerusalem.

History
Jefferson Davis.

ANSWERS
(QUIZ 7)

Team 1

Team 2

DRINKS ROUND

1	Nyasaland.	1	India.
2	Andy Capp.	2	Flash Gordon.
3	The Red Cross.	3	The Red Crescent.
4	Absinthe.	4	Maraschino.
5	Busby Berkeley.	5	Gene Kelly.
6	Persian or Pushtu.	6	Albania.
7	Jeffrey Archer.	7	Richard Eyre.
8	Montevideo.	8	Ulan Bator.
9	1972.	9	1983.
10	Tom Mix.	10	Max Brand.

RESERVE QUESTIONS

1 Aintree.
2 Eight.
3 Charles Macintosh.

Pub League Quiz 8 Answers

Team 1

ROUND 1
1 Basra.
2 Omnivores.
3 Ham, Shem and Japheth.
4 Lace.

5 Josiah Wedgwood.

ROUND 2
1 Sir Douglas Fairbanks, Charlie Chaplin, D.W. Griffith and Mary Pickford.
2 Oliver Cromwell (and Lord Leven).
3 Kingsley Amis.
4 Rocks formed by the cooling and solidifying of molten magmas.
5 Lanolin.

ROUND 3
1 Androcles.
2 A famous US jazz singer.
3 In your eyes.
4 Arthur Ashe.
5 Giacomo Puccini.

ROUND 4
1 The planet Pluto.
2 Mary Wells.
3 Thomas Alva Edison.
4 Electrocardiogram.

5 Tony Hancock.

Team 2

ROUND 1
1 Oran.
2 Invertebrate.
3 Rahab.
4 A window which tapers to an arched point.
5 Thomas Minton.

ROUND 2
1 Charlie Chaplin.

2 Edward I.

3 Hans Christian Andersen.
4 Lithosphere.

5 Ozone.

ROUND 3
1 Daedalus.
2 John Dankworth.
3 In your nose.
4 Four.
5 *Don Carlos*.

ROUND 4
1 A nebula.
2 Eleanor Rigby.
3 James Hargreaves.
4 Medical Research Council.
5 Una Stubbs.

ANSWERS
(QUIZ 8)

ROUND 5

Dress and fashion
Christian Dior.

Law
Impeachment.

Inventors and inventions
Sir James Dewar.

Famous men
Sigmund Freud.

Words
Intended for teaching or instructing.

Team 2

Team 1

ROUND 6
1   Durham.
2   The ugli.
3   Sheffield.
4   *The Sleepwalkers*.
5   Corsica.

1   Harvard.
2   The loganberry.
3   Manchester.
4   Budapest.
5   Tenerife.

ROUND 7
1   King Faisal I.
2   Woody Allen and Mia Farrow.
3   George Peppard.
4   John le Carré.
5   'Del Boy'.

1   Saud.
2   Tyne Daly.
3   Dirk Benedict.
4   R.D. Blackmore.
5   He played a mute.

ROUND 8
1   Three.
2   Pale blue and white.

3   London and Bristol.
4   Whitney Houston.
5   A terrier.

1   Prostitution.
2   'The Star-spangled Banner'.
3   1825.
4   Glasgow.
5   Cardiganshire, Pembrokeshire.

ROUND 9
1   The Lake District National Park.

2   Tasmania.
3   Austrian.
4   Old Trafford, Manchester.
5   Military Medal.

1   Octavia Hill, Sir Robert Hunter and Canon Hardwicke Rawnsley.
2   Sydney.
3   Polish.
4   Golf.

5   Minimum Lending Rate.

ROUND 10

Dress and fashion
Coco Chanel.

Law
Intestate.

Inventors and inventions
Charles Babbage.

Famous men
Dr Christian Barnard.

Words
Longsightedness.

Team 1

Team 2

DRINKS ROUND

1   George Meredith.
2   A rocking chair.
3   New Zealander.
4   Large marine fish.
5   Jean-François Millet.
6   Bobbysoxers.
7   Hg.
8   Sophomores.
9   Malt.
10 Nepal, Bhutan.

1   Beatrix Potter.
2   Raymond Baxter.
3   1912.
4   A leveret.
5   *Mona Lisa.*
6   The cornet.
7   Mg.
8   Sophism (sophistry).
9   A type of maize.
10 Natal.

ANSWERS
(QUIZ 9)

RESERVE QUESTIONS

1   Over 5,500.
2   0.6 seconds.
3   Plums.

Pub League Quiz 9 Answers

Team 1

Team 2

ROUND 1

1   John Lennon.
2   In the fabric of a
    cathedral.
3   Germaine Greer.

1   *Brothers in Arms.*
2   In a castle.
3   *Pride and Prejudice.*

112

4 New Zealand.
5 Confucius.

4 Joan of Arc.
5 The Bishop of Salisbury.

ROUND 2
1 Red.
2 Absent without leave.
3 Its prehistoric cave paintings.
4 The Penguin.
5 The Washington Monument.

1 Black.
2 Son of.
3 The horse.
4 Krypton.
5 The Spanish Steps.

ROUND 3
1 Brazil.
2 Brown.
3 Egypt.
4 Operation Barbarossa.
5 Natalie Wood.

1 Martina Navratilova.
2 Amtrak.
3 Shylock.
4 Operation Overlord.
5 Jayne Mansfield.

ROUND 4
1 Grenada.
2 Italian earthenware.
3 Aquarius.
4 *Women in Love*.
5 Paavo Nurmi.

1 On the Panama Canal.
2 Bread sticks.
3 Sirius.
4 Sir Walter Scott.
5 Jim Thorpe.

ANSWERS (QUIZ 9)

ROUND 5

Water life
A calf.

Television
Billy Connolly.

Organisations
Amnesty International.

Games
Contract bridge.

Flight
De Havilland.

Team 2

Team 1

ROUND 6
1 100 years.

1 Willy Wonka.

2 Dorothy.
3 Tin.
4 The Flying Bedstead.
5 The Statue of Liberty.

2 Jim Henson.
3 Australia.
4 The Tin Lizzie.
5 The Paris Exhibition of 1889.

ROUND 7

1 Middle class.
2 *Camelot.*
3 The emu.
4 *Morning Cloud.*
5 Biennially.

1 The House of Commons.
2 *The Rocky Horror Show.*
3 Sydney Harbour Bridge.
4 Robert E. Peary.
5 Cruiserweight.

ROUND 8

1 The flag of the United Kingdom.
2 Ulster Defence Regiment.
3 Amelia Earhart.
4 Spain.
5 Turkey.

1 The flag of Chile.
2 Basketball.
3 London (the Reform Club).
4 Lancashire.
5 Green.

ROUND 9

1 Aquavit.
2 *Gentlemen Prefer Blondes.*
3 Haile Selassie.
4 71 per cent.
5 The mosquito.

1 Gin.
2 Earl D. Biggers.
3 Nicholas Breakspear.
4 In the Arctic Ocean between Alaska and the North Pole.
5 German measles.

ROUND 10

Water life
The shark's.

Television
Mia Farrow.

Organisations
Khmer Rouge.

Games
Five.

Flight
Croydon.

Team 1	Team 2

DRINKS ROUND

	Team 1		Team 2
1	A French poodle.	1	The Uncle Remus books.
2	Tombstone, Arizona.	2	*High Noon*.
3	Mount Denali.	3	Alaska.
4	Oak-apples.	4	Yew trees.
5	Barbra Streisand.	5	El Cid.
6	Morocco.	6	Lake Victoria.
7	Poker.	7	Blackjack, pontoon.
8	The caribou or reindeer.	8	The antelope family.
9	George Stubbs.	9	John Constable.
10	Wiltshire.	10	London's British Museum.

RESERVE QUESTIONS
1 Three.
2 Melbourne.
3 Stephen Sondheim.

Pub League Quiz 10 Answers

Team 1	Team 2

ROUND 1

	Team 1		Team 2
1	Nashville.	1	Portland.
2	George Bernard Shaw.	2	Harold Pinter.
3	Knight, Order of St Patrick.	3	Member, Royal Victorian Order.
4	Longchamp.	4	Prix de L'Arc de Triomphe.
5	Gamal Abdel Nasser.	5	Mao Tse-tung.

ROUND 2

	Team 1		Team 2
1	Anode.	1	Cathode.
2	Le Mans.	2	Mike Hawthorn.
3	Marilyn Monroe.	3	Norma Jean Baker.
4	Loire.	4	Africa.
5	ZZ Top.	5	Wings.

ROUND 3

1 Anna Ford.
2 Benito Mussolini.
3 Anna Karenina.
4 A wild ass.
5 Four.

1 Anna Friel.
2 Il Duce.
3 Fyodor Dostoyevsky.
4 A breed of sheep.
5 Ramsay MacDonald, Clement Attlee, Harold Wilson and James Callaghan.

ROUND 4

1 Staffordshire.
2 *Breakfast at Tiffany's.*
3 The area of a parallelogram.
4 Birds' eggs.

5 Alaska.

1 The Cecils.
2 Henry Mancini.
3 Force.

4 The study of the origin and development of words.
5 Pennsylvania.

ROUND 5

Cathedrals
Rheims.

Heraldry
A term for colour which is used on a shield or coat of arms.

Numbers
Nine.

Who said?
Harold Wilson.

Soap operas
Brookside.

ANSWERS (QUIZ 10)

Team 2

Team 1

ROUND 6

1 Rudyard Kipling.
2 Richard Trevithick.
3 Normandy.

4 Allan-a-Dale.

5 Spain.

1 John Bunyan.
2 Worcester.
3 Ground almonds, sugar and egg white.
4 He helped to carry her off when she was about to be married to an old knight against her will.
5 USA (Kansas).

ROUND 7

1	The skin.	1	The brain.
2	Or.	2	Argent.
3	Vice-Admiral Sturdee.	3	Lord Kitchener.
4	Green Park.	4	Burlington House.
5	Red Indian (American).	5	Italian.

ROUND 8

1	Henrik Ibsen.	1	Oscar Wilde.
2	Andorra.	2	The Algarve.
3	Saltpetre or nitre.	3	Nitrous oxide.
4	Aphrodite.	4	Venus.
5	Thesaurus.	5	Concordance.

ROUND 9

1	Haemoglobin.	1	A hereditary defect that prevents blood clotting.
2	Dinghy.	2	Ski-ing.
3	Czech.	3	Maurice Ravel.
4	Edwin (Buzz) Aldrin.	4	Early Bird.
5	Supernova.	5	Mercury.

ROUND 10

Cathedrals
Aachen.

Heraldry
A knight's tunic emblazoned with the arms of the king or with his own coat of arms.

Numbers
18 and 30.

Who said?
Abraham Lincoln.

Soap operas
Grace Archer.

ANSWER.
(QUIZ 1(

Team 1

Team 2

DRINKS ROUND

1	International Atomic Energy Agency.	1	International Civil Aviation Organisation.
2	The Netherlands.	2	Maine, New Hampshire, Vermont, Rhode Island, Connecticut, Massachusetts.

3	H. Rider Haggard.	3	Charles Kingsley.
4	Jack Ruby.	4	Sirhan Sirhan.
5	Alfred the Great.	5	Macbeth.
6	Sophia Loren.	6	*Miranda*.
7	Wellington.	7	Luxembourg.
8	Silver.	8	Roy Rogers.
9	Fiona 3¾ and Jean 4½.	9	Edward 28 and Cyril 52.
10	Scotland.	10	Northern Ireland.

RESERVE QUESTIONS
1 Earl.
2 12.
3 Billiards.

Pub League Quiz 11 Answers

Team 1   *Team 2*

ROUND 1
1	Durham.	1	Somerset.
2	Portugal.	2	Bulgaria.
3	Baseball.	3	Gymnastics.
4	A set.	4	A drey.
5	1947.	5	Lord Louis Mountbatten of Burma.

NSWERS
QUIZ 11)

ROUND 2
1	Santiago.	1	Mexico City.
2	Georges Bizet.	2	Johannes Brahms.
3	Dislike or fear of strangers.	3	Rabies.
4	Prometheus.	4	The Gorgons.
5	Brian.	5	Ermintrude.

ROUND 3
1	Charles Bronson.	1	John Ford.
2	Charles Dickens.	2	Inspector Maigret.
3	An Arabian sailing ship.	3	A large Eskimo canoe.

4 70 minutes (2 × 35 minutes).
5 The Searchers.

4 Seven.

5 Bonnie Tyler.

ROUND 4
1 Hymen.
2 'SUCCESS'.
3 China (in the Tibetan Highlands).
4 Philately.
5 Smallpox.

1 Charon.
2 Katharine Hepburn.
3 Italy.

4 Butterfly specimens.
5 The liver.

ROUND 5

Films
Kid Galahad.

The arts
Paul Gauguin.

Literature
Anthony Trollope.

Sport
Point-to-point.

Proverbs
Repent at leisure.

Team 2

Team 1

ROUND 6
1 Lawrence of Arabia.
2 Randy Crawford.
3 The Fleur de Lys (the Prince of Wales' feathers).
4 Enid Blyton.
5 Albert Finney.

1 Arthur Miller.
2 Diana Ross.
3 A lion.
4 The 'Black Pig'.
5 Buster Keaton.

ROUND 7
1 A butterfly.
2 70.
3 Portuguese.
4 Six.
5 Leeds United.

1 A British sporting dog.
2 A tangent.
3 Spanish.
4 50.
5 Leicester City.

ANSWERS (QUIZ 11

ROUND 8
1 12.
2 Greece.
3 Henri de Toulouse-Lautrec.

1 11.
2 Belgium.
3 Jean Honoré Fragonard.

4 British Dental Association.	**4** Estimated Time of Departure.
5 *Juke Box Jury.*	**5** Jack Klugman.

ROUND 9

1 The Miners' Union.	**1** Prime Minister of Great Britain.
2 Louis XIV.	**2** Charles II.
3 Leeds.	**3** Southend-on-Sea.
4 Nebuchadnezzar.	**4** Peter and Philip.
5 Tommy Steele.	**5** Cat Stevens.

ROUND 10

Films	*Sport*
She Done Him Wrong.	Tottenham Hotspur.
The arts	*Proverbs*
Leonardo da Vinci.	Good intentions.
Literature	
Caesura.	

Team 1

Team 2

DRINKS ROUND

1 Addis Ababa.	**1** Lerwick.
2 *Hans Christian Andersen.*	**2** George Lucas.
3 *Madame Butterfly.*	**3** Gilbert and Sullivan.
4 Lead.	**4** Copper.
5 The telephone.	**5** The Chinese.
6 Canada.	**6** Rifle shooting.
7 A mongoose.	**7** Ants.
8 The Torridge.	**8** River Nene.
9 The Doors.	**9** 10 CC.
10 Baseball.	**10** Billiards.

RESERVE QUESTIONS

1 Uranus.
2 St Stanilaus.
3 Germany.

Pub League Quiz 12 Answers

Team 1

ROUND 1
1   Forget-me-not.
2   In a library. It is a system for classifying books.
3   Ellery Queen.
4   Darlington, Co. Durham.
5   Venezuela.

ROUND 2
1   The Dave Clark Five
2   Dr Johnson.
3   26.
4   Fair Isle.
5   Marie Stopes.

ROUND 3
1   1969.

2   Redingote.
3   A rock climber.
4   The gift of prophecy.
5   Master of the Rolls.

ROUND 4
1   Tagus.
2   Marshal of the Royal Air Force.
3   Its Wall Game.
4   La Mancha.
5   Harry.

Team 2

ROUND 1
1   Hyacinth.
2   In the sky. It is a star group.
3   William Shakespeare.
4   Weymouth.
5   Belgium.

ROUND 2
1   Elvis Costello
2   George Orwell.
3   12.
4   Triassic.
5   Dr Thomas Barnardo.

ROUND 3
1   1955 (allow one year either way).
2   Gaberdine.
3   Tug-of-war.
4   Saturday, after Saturn.
5   'My Lord'.

ROUND 4
1   The River Moskva.
2   Through hardship to the stars.
3   Old Kent Road.
4   *1984.*
5   Connie Francis.

ANSWERS (QUIZ 12)

ROUND 5 *Individual questions for team*

Pop music
Fairport Convention.

The Olympics
None (the USA boycotted the games, held in Moscow).

The Bible
Daniel.

What comes next?
Seven; they are numbers around a dartboard.

Where is it?
North Island, New Zealand.

Team 2

Team 1

ROUND 6

	Team 2		Team 1
1	Hydrology.	1	Metallurgy.
2	In your throat at the back of your mouth.	2	The outermost layer of the skin.
3	William Pitt, first Earl of Chatham.	3	Harold Macmillan.
4	Crete.	4	Cologne.
5	*Mansfield Park* by Jane Austen.	5	Mary Shelley.

ROUND 7

	Team 2		Team 1
1	Deuteronomy.	1	The feeding of the five thousand.
2	Finland.	2	The krone.
3	Crabs.	3	A snake.
4	Columbia Broadcasting System.	4	Royal Academy of Dramatic Art.
5	Two over par for a hole.	5	Nine.

ROUND 8

ANSWERS (QUIZ 12)

	Team 2		Team 1
1	35.	1	Christmas Day.
2	The Queen of Hearts in *Alice in Wonderland*.	2	*Tess of the d'Urbervilles*.
3	The British national anthem, 'God Save the King'.	3	George and Ira Gershwin.
4	Oliver.	4	Jefferson.
5	Lord Scarman.	5	Winston S. Churchill.

ROUND 9

1 *Macbeth.*
2 A hog.
3 The bicycle.
4 The dollar.
5 A bat.

1 *Twelfth Night.*
2 A jenny.
3 The Montgolfier brothers.
4 The dinar.
5 A diving sea-duck.

ROUND 10

Pop music
The Scaffold.

The Olympics
Jesse Owens.

The Bible
Abraham.

What comes next?
Richard Nixon.

Where is it?
The Louvre, Paris.

Team 1

Team 2

DRINKS ROUND

1 George IV.
2 Cheese.
3 Norwich City.
4 John Cabot.
5 Caustic soda.
6 Peru and Bolivia.
7 Argentina.
8 The Wurzels.
9 Zsa Zsa Gabor.
10 Windsor Castle.

1 James I (VI of Scotland).
2 Oysters.
3 Luton Town.
4 Dutch.
5 Epsom salts.
6 Canada.
7 Chaim Weizzman.
8 T. Rex.
9 Tony Benn.
10 Coventry Cathedral.

RESERVE QUESTIONS

1 Pete Townsend.
2 Kentucky.
3 Angels on horseback.

Pub League Quiz 13 Answers

Team 1

Team 2

ROUND 1

1 Damascus.

1 Ankara.

2 Alfred, Lord Tennyson, ('The Charge of The Light Brigade').
3 British Academy of Film and Television Arts.
4 Turpentine.
5 Australia.

2 George Bernard Shaw.

3 National Union of Journalists.
4 French polish.
5 Tunbridge Wells.

ROUND 2
1 Nottinghamshire.
2 The eye.
3 Scott Joplin.
4 Perth.
5 Meat Loaf.

1 Warwickshire.
2 The skin.
3 Jacques Offenbach.
4 Armagh.
5 Gene Pitney.

ROUND 3
1 Mount Olympus.
2 Richard I, William II (William Rufus) and Harold II.
3 Sylvester Stallone.
4 Stanley Spencer.
5 Aviation, particularly helicopters.

1 Helicon.
2 Richard II.

3 Robert Redford.
4 Rembrandt.
5 Jet propulsion.

ROUND 4
1 Juniper.
2 A mast or sail.

3 Zinc and copper.
4 Johnny Horton.
5 The Boer War.

1 Rum.
2 A vessel of hot water in which cooking pans are slowly heated.
3 Mercury.
4 Kenneth Roberts.
5 The Battle of Jutland.

ROUND 5
Entertainment
Lee Strasberg.

Finance
The Dow Jones Index.

Words
Fire.

Music
Glenn Miller.

ANSWERS (QUIZ 13)

Industry
Cotton.

Team 2	Team 1

ROUND 6

Team 2	Team 1
1 Garrick Street.	1 Poste Restante.
2 The Swiss Guard.	2 The Quakers.
3 Basketball.	3 Baseball.
4 The Taj Mahal.	4 St Paul's Cathedral.
5 Sculpture.	5 Opera.

ROUND 7

Team 2	Team 1
1 Pedro Cabral.	1 Francisco de Orellana.
2 Venus.	2 Neptune.
3 The development of the atomic bomb in the Second World War.	3 The fields of Flanders were covered with poppies.
4 Trigonometry.	4 9.20.
5 The Hollies.	5 Otis Redding.

ROUND 8

Team 2	Team 1
1 Tunisia.	1 William the Conqueror.
2 Devon.	2 Telford (Thomas Telford).
3 Bouvier.	3 Marie Antoinette.
4 Turmeric.	4 Chicory.
5 Orthopaedics.	5 Spoonerism.

ROUND 9

Team 2	Team 1
1 Libra.	1 Aries.
2 Anwar Sadat.	2 Julius Caesar.
3 *Dallas*.	3 Stephanie Beacham.
4 The 'Pathétique'.	4 The 'Choral' Symphony.
5 Melancholy.	5 Melanin.

ROUND 10

Team 2

Entertainment
Atlanta.

Words
'I came, I saw, I conquered'.

Industry
Hops.

Team 1

Finance
Gross National Product.

Music
Leonard Bernstein.

Team 1	Team 2

DRINKS ROUND

Team 1	Team 2
1 Catch 22.	**1** For example.
2 Measuring blood pressure.	**2** Ringing in the ears.
3 Herbs.	**3** They are the old names for the fingers and thumb of the hand.
4 A kettledrum.	**4** Gondoliers.
5 Anthony Fokker.	**5** Wernher von Braun.
6 The diaphragm.	**6** The shoulder blade.
7 Georges Seurat.	**7** Andy Warhol.
8 Franklin D. Roosevelt.	**8** Abraham Lincoln.
9 Little Minch.	**9** Off Anglesey, North Wales.
10 Anthony Eden.	**10** Golda Meir.

RESERVE QUESTIONS
1   Television.
2   The Northwest Passage.
3   Irene.

Pub League Quiz 14 Answers

Team 1	Team 2

ROUND 1

Team 1	Team 2
1 Charles I.	**1** Typhoid fever.
2 *The Toilet of Venus.*	**2** The picture of Dorian Gray.
3 104.	**3** 94.
4 James II.	**4** Cavaliers.
5 The eight of diamonds.	**5** Mahjong.

ROUND 2

Team 1	Team 2
1 A skylark.	**1** T.S. Eliot.
2 Tahiti.	**2** Antrim.
3 A single horse hair.	**3** Cronus.
4 Wonderbra.	**4** Pierre Cardin.
5 Modest Mussorgsky.	**5** Bela Bartok.

ROUND 3

1 Ernest Hemingway.
2 The west coast of the USA, centred on San Francisco.
3 The edible entrails of a deer or other animal.
4 Joe Mercer.
5 Inter-Continental Ballistic Missile.

1 Catherine Cookson.
2 Sri Lanka.
3 Small dumplings made of potatoes, flour or semolina.
4 Stanley Matthews.
5 Strategic Arms Limitation Talks.

ROUND 4

1 Freetown.
2 A bomber.
3 Clara Peggotty.
4 Wolverhampton.
5 Dail Eireann.

1 Kingston.
2 France.
3 Peter Mayle.
4 Hyde Park.
5 Niccolo Machiavelli.

ROUND 5

The Bible
The Acts of the Apostles.

Opera
Don Giovanni.

Mythology
Ra.

Trees and plants
Elm.

Games and pastimes
Diabolo.

Team 2

Team 1

ROUND 6

1 Four.
2 The one nearest the stern.
3 St James's Palace.
4 Edward de Bono.
5 Zambia.

1 Duodenum.
2 Two.
3 A gaol.
4 John Flamsteed's.
5 Death Valley, California.

ROUND 7

1 Benjamin Disraeli.
2 Cornwall.
3 Ballet.
4 1910.
5 Apples.

1 John le Carré.
2 Edinburgh.
3 Graham Sutherland.
4 King John.
5 Oranges.

ANSWERS (QUIZ 14)

127

ROUND 8
1 20.
2 A type of heavy draught horse.
3 Six.
4 Robin Day.
5 A mule.

ROUND 9
1 Queen Catherine (of Aragon).
2 Cataract.
3 Purdah.
4 Jonathan Swift.
5 1966.

ROUND 10
The Bible
Bathsheba.

Opera
Yeoman of the Guard.

Mythology
Daphne.

Team 1

1 150.
2 The making of dictionaries.
3 Pete Sampras.
4 Robert Robinson.
5 Basenji.

1 Ophelia's.

2 In the neck.
3 Jehad.
4 Irwin Shaw.
5 Gary Kasparov.

Trees and plants
Tuber.

Games and pastimes
The Queen of Spades.

Team 2

DRINKS ROUND
1 Harold Macmillan.
2 *Middlemarch.*
3 Nellie the Elephant.
4 The Nile.
5 Carrots.
6 A small writing desk.
7 Patricia Highsmith's.
8 Des O'Connor.
9 *The Far Pavilions.*
10 Action on Health and Smoking.

1 Benjamin Disraeli.
2 Samuel Butler.
3 Looby-Loo.
4 Morocco.
5 Cauliflower.
6 A glass container used in distilling.
7 Agatha Christie's.
8 Rolf Harris.
9 *The Wind in the Willows.*
10 Extra-sensory perception.

RESERVE QUESTIONS
1 *Hard Times.*

2 Morphine (Morpheus).
3 One.